D1253982

THE UNIVERSE AND YOU

THE UNIVERSE AND YOU

by

HELEN HOWELL NEAL

On the basis of a manuscript
by Herbert Vincent Neal

CARLBORG-BLADES INC.

MANUFACTURED IN THE UNITED STATES OF AMERICA
BY THE COLONIAL PRESS INC., CLINTON, MASS.

Affectionately dedicated to JANET GRIEG POST and to each of the many eager, responsive students who made possible this adventure into Theoretical Biology

Foreword

Herbert Neal was first of all a biologist, and an impressive teacher of the advancing body of biological knowledge. He was devoted to his science and to the methods of science; he communicated that devotion to his students. But as a man, he was bound to ask himself whether the methods of biological science were adequate to give us the full truth about man. This question is one whose importance grows with the years, for it is a matter of the highest practical consequence what man thinks of himself and what inferences he draws from that thought about his own business on the planet and his own destiny.

It was characteristic of Neal that he gave to this question an answer of whose truth he was fully convinced and which, at the same time, was wholly undogmatic. He believed that there is more in human nature than either biology or psychology or sociology can reveal. Yet he was wholly unwilling to press his conviction on his readers, as he was unwilling to press it upon his students, by pure affirmation. He preferred to show by patient enquiry the difficulties one encounters in simply identifying the man with his biological nature, the processes of his organism, or in equating the history of his body, its evolution and dissolution, with the career of the person as "mind," and then to invite the reader to draw his own conclusions.

The Universe and You is an outgrowth of Neal's years of teaching at Knox College and then at Tufts College. His courses, known as "Man's Place in Nature" and "Theoretical Biology," evolved through the advances of science and the questions of his students. Their problems suggested the need of this book. It might be described as a course in the emergence of philosophy out of biology. It is something more than philosophy; it is the birth of reflection about man and the world from the direct encounter with science, at the frontier of its enquiry into truth. It raises the wish that the philosopher latent in every scientist might come to a similar clarity and candor in the statement of what remains to be known.

Death leaves no thinker the choice at what stage his work shall be interrupted. Some manuscripts have been left all but complete; some have been barely outlined. In this case the plan was made, and much of the writing done; but there were large gaps, and the question was an open one whether a completion could be attempted. In the nature of the work, it was not a biological supplement that was needed; nor yet a philosophical supplement. It was the carrying out of a point of view, characteristic of the author, into a wealth of material embracing parts of the area of many sciences. It could be done, if at all, only by one to whom that view was second nature.

As the work now stands completed, it is a joint labor of Herbert Neal and Helen Neal, his wife, herself a biologist and teacher. She has, by her own courageous and able effort, preserved for our time a wealth of material constituting a cumulative argument, the philosophic fruit of Neal's life-work. She has brought the scientific material up-to-date and reorganized the arrangement. The resulting expression is in her language. But the major outlines of the discussion are those of Herbert Neal, and the message of these pages is one which this age has great cause to heed.

William Ernest Hocking
Harvard University

Notes on Herbert Vincent Neal

Herbert Vincent Neal, whose teachings are the basis of this book written for the general reader by his scholarly and distinguished widow, was a scientist of eminence, a teacher of arresting power and a profound philosophical thinker.

It was my good fortune to have been a student of Dr. Neal's from 1917 to 1921 at Tufts College. During this time as a major student in biology, I took all of Dr. Neal's courses and assisted him for one year in his course in general zoology and for two years in his course in comparative anatomy. In the thirty years which have passed since that time, my gratitude has increased for the good fortune I had in knowing Dr. Neal so well.

Dr. Neal's "Theoretical Biology" was the greatest intellectual experience of my undergraduate life. Then and now the mind and spirit of this notable teacher seem to me to tower above ordinary minds. The topics we wrestled with were fundamental, persistent, challenging and ultimately spiritual. Above all, he made his students feel a lasting concern about understanding the growth of man's physical and mental life, the problems of his origin and destiny.

Herbert Vincent Neal was born at Lewiston, Maine, in 1869. He died in 1940. He received his Bachelor's degree from Bates College. Later he received a second Bachelor's degree and Master's degree and the degree of Doctor of Philosophy from Harvard University. Bates subsequently awarded him the honorary degree of Doctor of Science.

After his graduate study in Cambridge, he spent a year in further study and investigation at the University of Munich in Germany. He returned to America and became Professor of Biology of Knox College in Illinois. After sixteen years at this post, he came to Tufts College, succeeding John Sterling Kingsley as Professor of Biology. From 1913 to 1939, when he retired, he was head of the Department of Biology. For twelve years, he was also Dean of the Graduate School.

Dr. Neal was actively interested in various marine biological laboratories. He served as Director of the Harpswell and later of the Mount Desert Island Laboratories in Maine. He was a member of the Corporation of the Marine Biological Laboratory at Woods Hole and of the Bermuda Biological Station.

He fully recognized the importance of work for scientific societies in advancing the cause of academic understanding in America. He was Secretary of the Zoological Section of the American Association for the Advancement of Science. He was President of the American Society of Zoologists, a member of the Association of American Anatomists, a Fellow of the American Academy of Arts and Sciences, and a Corresponding Member of the Russian National Academy of Science. He was an active member of Phi Beta Kappa and Sigma Xi.

The field of embryology claimed Dr. Neal's chief research

endeavors. He was an expert authority on the segmental structure and the growth of the vertebrate head. This led him to have a deep interest in the embryology of the cranial nerves and the eye muscles. He also wrote on general biological questions. He was the author, with collaboration from Herbert W. Rand of Harvard, of two important books, *Comparative Anatomy* and *Chordate Anatomy*. These are advanced-level textbooks still widely used as authoritative books in a field studied by nearly all American biologists and premedical students.

In his own courses in zoology, anatomy and embryology, he insisted upon scientific understanding and technical precision. It was in his course in theoretical biology, however, that the undergradute student first felt that he came to know his teacher intimately. This notable course was limited to students who had already demonstrated an interest in biology. The subject of evolution was the underlying topic of the year. The growth of the inorganic world was considered.

It is certain that no thoughtful student who fully participated in Dr. Neal's advanced courses could ever again accept a simple, uncritical, nineteenth century materialism as a basis for the understanding of the embryology of the body or the development of man's mentality.

With the help of this book, the honest and intelligent reader may formulate his own view in regard to the questions with which it deals. Dr. Neal did not wish to make converts or disciples. He was intent upon helping college students develop into thinking men and women. This transforming influence was his greatest achievement, a living, ever-growing memorial. No book can be as vital a force as was his way of living and of sharing his philosophy of life. A book, however, may pass on to developing thinkers the active leaven of such warm vitality. Its thought about life and man's place in the universe has permanent significance never more actual than now.

LEONARD CARMICHAEL
Secretary of the Smithsonian
Institution,
and from 1938 to 1953
President of Tufts College

Acknowledgments

My thanks go out warmly to the dear friends and colleagues of my husband, whose generous encouragement and constructive criticism have heartened me by their full measure of devotion to him.

Chief among them are the writers of the foreword, William Ernest Hocking, and of the Notes on Herbert Vincent Neal, Leonard Carmichael; also Dr. Leon Campbell; Dr. Russell Carpenter; Mrs. Marion Bunbury Cater; Dr. William H. Cole; Dr. Edna Heidbreder; Dr. Leonard Mead; Dr. Robert L. Nichols; Dr. Chloe B. Owings; Dr. Herbert W. Rand; Dr. Kenneth D. Roeder; Miss Mary Russell; Mrs. Dorothy Dean Scott; Rt. Rev. Jonathan G. Sherman; Dr. Homer W. Smith; Dr. Paul A. Warren; Mr. William H. Wells; Dr. John A. Wheeler. To these names many another deserves to be added with warm thanks.

For the courtesy accorded me by the publishers from whose books extracts are given in the notes at the end of the book, I am deeply grateful.

HELEN H. NEAL,
Salisbury Cove, Maine

TABLE OF CONTENTS

CHAPTER ONE

The Universe and Our Planet

The starry skies are dimmed for us by electric street lights. The position of the sun and stars in the heavens no longer determines seed time and harvest. The seasonal character of foods vanishes before modern methods of refrigeration and transportation. The rigors of winter are tempered by the activities of a tiny thermostat. The rhythms of day and night become more relative than actual. Thus the seeming importance of nature, the realm of natural objects and forces, materials and laws retreats steadily in our perspective as our experience becomes increasingly composed of man-made factors. We possess a fast-growing accumulation of scientific facts about our expanding universe but a shrinking amount of direct personal experience with it and its ways. Our cosmic outlook contracts!

Yet the persistent problems of our relation to nature, the wide world of natural substances and occurrences, and of nature's relation to us remain unsolved. What is nature's source and significance? Is there behind it an expression of mind and purpose? Is there a directive factor in nature? Or is nature a series of chance elements and events?

For the Taoists, the way of nature was tzujan: it came of itself. Many of us believe that nature has a source beyond itself. Neither belief can be verified. It may seem to take more faith to believe that chance determines not only the illimitable range but also each infinitesimal detail of nature than to believe that there is in our universe something more than nature, something directive behind the interrelated laws to which nature conforms. To believe that nature has a source beyond itself may give it a larger significance than to deny such a source. To fail to prove such a belief, by the ordinary methods of science, does not disprove it. The quest of this book is to examine evidence on both sides of the question: "Is there a directive factor in our universe, or is nature an aggregate of chance happenings and chance elements?"

Nature, the world of natural phenomena, of knowable facts, is the field with which science deals, but scientific investigation does not always reveal ultimate realities. Scientists, however, make no claim that all reality is covered by their studies. Science is a methodology dealing with data which can be observed, measured, and proved. These limitations are self-imposed by the character of its method. Beyond these limits science does not usually try to answer questions, not because they are unimportant, but because they cannot be answered by scientific methods. Science, however, through its facts supplies our quest with important clues.

There are many matters which we cannot know through

science with its dependence upon sensory observations and amplifying instruments. When scientists cannot know by proof, they may make assumptions which they test by experimental procedure. If an experiment verifies the likely truth of the assumption, they continue to believe it. If the experiment refutes the assumption, they must seek another. This accounts for discarded beliefs. Interpretation is based on knowledge of fact. When knowledge is lacking, insight may penetrate further and reveal the significance of whatever facts are known, thereby aiding the correct assumption.

The true goal of science is the enlarging of man's understanding of nature, but this wisdom cannot stop short of the ultimate questions of source and significance. These, in the light of our present knowledge, must be matters of assumption and interpretation based on insight and faith, as were the facts about radioactivity before visible traces of electronic behavior in experiments with Wilson cloud chambers demonstrated electrons as true.

Science has disclosed order and harmony in the universe. The interrelatedness of its laws suggest further unities so that the mastery of any special field demands seeing it in relation to the rest of science and integrating it with all accepted knowledge. This is a lifelong task but one to which you may lift your eyes with hope and thanksgiving.

Until the beginning of this century, modern astronomy had centered its studies largely on our solar system. Now the problems are more likely to be those of energy generation in stars, why they keep on shining, the relative abundancies of the chemical elements in the universe, or the distribution of the far-flung galaxies in space. In 1924 the new

100-inch telescope on Mt. Wilson showed that the faint group of stars known as the Andromeda nebula was actually thousands of times farther away than any single star known. It showed a disk-shaped stellar system or galaxy isolated from other groups. Its stars were like in type and arrangement to near-by stars. Thus it was established that "our stars" were also organized into a spiral shaped galaxy, a twin of Andromeda, in which our sun and its planets lay a considerable distance from one of the edges of the plate-like whole. Peering outward toward the rim of the plate, we look along the flattened or greatest diameter of the group and see the stars of our galaxy close-packed in what we call the Milky Way. This is a thin disk of interstellar gas and stars. It is estimated that the total quantity of material comprising interstellar gas seems to be even greater than all the material in all the stars combined. This gas controls not only the motion of the stars, but also their birth and the rates at which they grow, as well as their evolution.

Now that the 200-inch Hale long range telescope on Palomar Mountain is in use, we have wonderful new and detailed photographs of galaxies. It can look a billion light-years into space, yet it gives only a gimlet-eyed view like peeping at a ball park through a nail hole in a fence. It has been wonderful to have the work of this triumph in telescope-building supplemented by the wide, sharp field of the big Schmidt 48-inch telescope also on Mt. Palomar. The promise of future revelations is bright, the tests of expansion surer.

In the great dome of night, if the sky is clear, about five thousand stars are visible to us at one time without a telescope. The nearest one is 25 million million miles away, its light reaching us in 4.28 years, traveling at the rate of 186,-366 miles a second. These stars together with about one hundred billion fainter ones are estimated as forming our galaxy. Our sun with its planets is but a tiny part of the whole. Our small earth circles around a mighty sun more than a million times its size and about ninety-three million miles away. This great sun is just an average-sized star, and its solar system of 9 planets seen from afar would look like a faint and microscopic blur upon the unimaginably vast dome of the heavens. Many other such galaxies exist; perhaps a dozen or fifteen are within a million light-years of us, a light-year (the distance light can travel in a year) measuring 5.88 trillion miles. From recent surveys it appears that galaxies may be counted by the billions without reaching their limit. If your spirit quails under the account of such numbers and distances, you may take sanctuary in the amazing achievements of the human mind. Shapley tells us that the "universe of galaxies is expanding at a rate that at best doubles the radius in 13 hundred million years; but our knowledge of the universe trebles in one generation." [1]

After stretching the horizons of our minds by such outer reaches, our nearer neighbors, the sun and its planets, need to be brought freshly into focus. A map, accurate in its scale (such as described by Russell, 1940), will help us realize the isolation of our solar system. On this map "Pluto at its remotest is a foot from the sun, the earth's orbit only half an inch across and Jupiter an inch and a quarter from the sun; but the nearest star would be a full mile away." [2] The rest of the group of 100 billion stars that are said to compose our galaxy are spread over a space so vast that light needs 100 thousand years to go from one side to the other.

Not only is our solar system isolated by its remoteness from the stars of its galaxy, but it is unique among such systems by its complexity. We know some double stars—about 10 per cent are such—a few triple, some quadruple, but the largest number of bodies thus far known in the family of any star, except our sun, is 6 (Pollux), all stars. In our solar system there are the sun, 9 large planets, 28 satellites belonging to 6 of these planets; an estimated 1000 asteroids; probably 100 thousand comets.

The spectroscope reveals that all the diverse members of our solar system as well as the entire stellar universe, of which the sun and its planets are so small a part, are composed of the same kinds of chemical elements in varying proportions. In the sun 60 are identified, 40 in another star and so on. Astronomers can tell us with confidence that the same elements are found throughout all matter everywhere. These elements give off radiation of different wave lengths whose lines and bands may be photographed and identified when separated by the prisms of a spectroscope. Thus the composition of the most distant visible stars can be known.

Temperatures may also be known through spectroscopic analysis since the radiation of a glowing body varies as the temperature rises or falls. The spectroscope, greatly aided by Palomar's eye, also indicates the motion of the stars of galaxies toward or away from us, and the velocity of their motion.

We cannot know how long the arrangement and motion of the various bodies in our solar system have been maintained, but we know that for the period called "Historical Time" the calculated historical eclipses agree with "at the time" records made during the building of the pyramids and other accurately dated events. In some cases they have served to correct present accepted chronology.

We marvel at the fierce energies liberated by our sun and by the stars, all of which must be considered suns. The dependence of plants upon sunlight leads us to infer that our sun was shining during the life of the early plant forms found as fossils in rocks laid down a billion years ago. It has probably been shining ever since, very much as it does now, for it is estimated that if the sun's surface temperature were to change by as much as 10 per cent, life on earth would probably be extinguished. Had the sun been pure carbon with just enough oxygen to keep it burning, the whole would have burned out long ago. Nor could the more efficient but still inadequate source of energy known as gravitational contraction account for such quantity and duration of energy, though it might raise internal temperatures to points making other sources available.

For a time it was thought that radioactivity might account for the sun's energy. But the rate of radiation from uranium never changes, and were the sun wholly made of that material, the energy released would be inadequate. Since the spectroscope shows in the sun some 59 other elements—hydrogen, helium, carbon, oxygen, nitrogen, etc., it is known that, whatever degree of radioactivity goes on, its reduction of mass into energy would be a small part of the energy pouring its power so bountifully into space.

The extremely high internal temperature of stars is an

important factor in their energy production. According to Eddington's theory, this may be as high as 40 million degrees Fahrenheit. At such temperatures the constituent particles are moving about so forcefully that nuclear transformations are produced. These may vary in different stars, but all of them release vast quantities of energy and involve transmutation of the elements.

A star like our sun shines by converting hydrogen into helium. To keep on shining at its present rate, our sun, an unassuming dwarf whose center is little less than half a million miles from its surface, must convert 564 million tons of hydrogen into 560 million tons of helium every second. All the steps in this transformation worked out by Bethe of Cornell, are fairly well established by experiment. The very complicated process has been simply stated by him for the layman. "Hydrogen supplies the fuel, helium forms the ashes while carbon and nitrogen keep the process going by a chain of reactions at the end of which they are formed anew." [3]

The origin of the solar system is one of the most perplexing problems facing astronomers. The Laplace Theory (1796) and the Tidal Theory (about 1919) both proved defective. But early in 1948 a completely new and strikingly simple theory was put forward by Whipple of the Harvard Observatory. He believes that the cosmic dust which drifts in great smoke-like puffs through interstellar space is the raw material from which our universe evolved. One such puff may have given birth to our sun, the earth, and other planets and all their satellites. This cloud is estimated to have been perhaps 5 trillion miles in diameter and almost impossibly light, having only one tiny frozen particle of matter to every 5 cubic yards of space. Other such clouds have been measured by astronomers where they have been observed in the Milky Way. Some believe that there is continuous creation of background material and that the universe has an infinite future in which all its very large scale features will be preserved.

Driven day and night by the force of starlight, such clouds converged until sufficient weight gave a center of gravity around which other masses swirled. The motion drew more matter toward the swirling masses. The drag of particles striking the inner-sides caused the more solid masses to rotate. Increasing contraction may have set up shock waves so that the great cloud suddenly collapsed, forming one central incandescent sun. Meantime the stream of smaller masses of matter, which had been spiraling in and rotating, was left suspended in space as planets. Friction, developed by these rapidly moving masses, heated them to high temperatures, as fragments of meteorites are heated when they hurl through our atmosphere to fall upon the earth.

Astronomers long thought the compactness of our planetary system and its orderly state was due to a common origin and some process of evolution. Now they are confident that both sun and massive planets are formed from cosmic dust.

Turning from our universe to consider our planet, we may feel more at home. But we must view this earth of ours in the light of its probable evolution. For countless eons of its past, from cosmic dust, through intense heat fusing its dust into molten rock, through cloud-enwrapping moisture to condensation of its seas, this earth of ours has gone cycling on around its sun. Its atmosphere, its rock and soil, its seas have all had a long evolution. Before considering these, it is essential that we all accept the changed concept of matter which has been established as a result of the revolutionary discoveries of the last six decades. These include X-rays (1895); radioactivity; the relationships of elements as arranged in the table of atomic numbers; the acceptance of the behavior of all matter, living and non-living, as electrical (except magnetic fields, gravitation and atomic fission); and the development of the science of electronics with its radio, radar, sonar, and television.

In any form—solid, liquid or gas—matter is thought of as "frozen" into electric particles with electrons revolving about a tiny nucleus of protons and neutrons. These energy-systems are called *atoms.* Atoms of the same kind joined together form *elements* such as oxygen, carbon, or iron. Atoms of different kinds unite into the combinations we call *molecules* either by sharing or transferring electrons. The new knowledge of the structure of atoms has brought new understanding of the forces that unite them and hold them together. Also it explains why chemists are able to make synthetic mixtures and various compounds. These atoms and molecules make up not only our rocks and stars, our air and oceans, but also all our common objects such as furniture, fabrics and foods. They also make the dynamic, living energy-systems which we call cells and describe as alive.

When Rutherford suggested (1904) the revolutionary hypothesis which reduced the baffling and complicated observations of radioactivity to a simple hypothesis, he taught that not all atoms are eternally stable, having existed from the beginning of time and likely to continue to its end, as had been previously believed. Some atoms in nature are actively unstable, exploding with sudden violence. These compose the naturally radioactive substances; the observed penetrating rays are the fragments given off by the atomic explosions.

The substances of earth had long been the special study of chemists. They arranged the elements in a table according to their weights. Although relationships were indicated, the troublesome fractions were puzzling.

Roentgen's discovery in 1895 of X-rays gave a new means of exploring *atoms and elements.* No one has ever seen an atom, but much that we know about them grew out of the study of the nature of X-rays. Atoms were now accurately located by means of X-rays and a few simple mathematical formulas, and a close estimate of their size could be obtained. The electrical nature of matter had been discovered, but as yet the individual character of each kind of atom was unknown. Using each element as a target in an X-ray tube, a beam of electrons was fired at each in succession. The X-rays from the tube were of two kinds, one of which was characteristic of the target element. Thus the atoms of each element were forced to give an autograph in the form of different characteristic X-ray wave lengths. These waves when studied showed close relationships. They arranged themselves in several series of beautiful regularity with a few blank spaces indicating missing elements. There were positions for 92 kinds of atoms, from hydrogen (1) to uranium (92). The strange irregularities that presented themselves in the arrangement by weights were lacking; not a single exception appeared.

It had been thought that new types of atoms might be

discovered in the stars, but to date the spectroscope shows that even the most distant ones seem to be made of the same materials as those we know. Four artificially produced elements are now added to the 92 naturally occurring elements, but the facts of radioactivity make it difficult to build any new elements which are at all permanent.

Meantime just before World War I, the whole conception of matter and electricity was revolutionized. Rutherford had suggested that each atom was a tiny solar system with electrons for planets. Bohr made his famous comment that there were only certain possible orbits in which electrons could rotate. If an atom had many planetary electrons such as uranium with 92, these must be grouped in orbits of different sizes. Today with further perfection of X-ray methods, the way in which the electrons in the 92 different kinds of atoms are grouped can be stated with growing confidence.

Something of still greater importance came out of this work. It was suggested that the atomic numbers must designate the total number of net positive charges on the nucleus. Rutherford's experiments confirmed this. Out of all this has come our concept of the plan or architecture of atoms. The positive charges on the various nuclei run from 1 to 92 for 92 different types of atoms corresponding to what are now called atomic numbers. The external electrons in exactly the same number are grouped about the nucleus.

The ideas of Rutherford and Bohr on the strutcture of atoms are now firmly established, but with additions. The nucleus of an atom, around which the planetary electrons whirl, consists of a closely packed group of neutrons and protons, elementary building blocks of nature, some two thousand times heavier than the electrons, so that the nucleus contains practically all the atom's matter and indeed energy. In Lawrence's graphic words, the "protons and neutrons are visualized as extremely small, dense spheres of matter, so small indeed that if an atom were as large as a cathedral on the same scale the nucleus of the atom would be no larger than a fly." [4] The protons carry positive charges of electricity, and the number of protons in the nucleus equals the number of planetary electrons (negative); hence the atom as a whole is electrically uncharged. In other words, the nucleus of an atom contains a number of protons equal to its atomic number in the periodic table: for instance, hydrogen 1, uranium 92, curium (one of the artificial ones) 96. Neutrons, however, are electrically uncharged, and accordingly the number of neutrons in the nucleus does not affect the planetary electrons. Varying the number of neutrons in the nucleus alters only the weight of the atom. Thus it is that we have isotopes of the elements—atoms of the same atomic number but of different weights.

Today we know that the arrangement of particles is what gives to each atom its chemical and physical properties and we know how each is centered about a nucleus of definite structure, a thousand million million times smaller than the atom itself. The table of atomic numbers summarizes facts and relationships and simplifies the study of elements. It reveals a fundamental regularity, a deep order in nature, the nature to which we belong with our questing minds seeking to understand the whole.

This simplified idea of the structure of matter is adequate to explain the fundamental theory of electronics if you remember that whirling electrons can be separated from the influence of the nucleus. The static electricity due to friction is a good example of this. Brushing the hair on a dry day may remove electrons from the molecular structure of the hair so that each hair acquires the same charge and repels and is repelled by its neighbors.

Electronics has shown us how electrons can be separated from the influence of the nucleus and put to useful work. The medium of this separation is the vacuum tube with a long history of experimentation behind it. The discovery of space-charge law governing the flow of electrons in a high vacuum has harnessed the power of electrons for all time. They are no longer locked within atoms, or wirebound, or surging through space uncontrolled. They can be isolated in a high vacuum tube free from wires, and a new control can be established. These tubes now number hundreds of varieties. Still the heart of radio, television, radar and sonar, these tubes and their flexible valves also work for the doctor, the fire-warden, the policeman and the industrialist, and they help in many another human undertaking. They make possible the amazing instruments computing the varying factors in hitting targets from moving vessels or planes. They are the basis of the new modern miracle, the analyzing and calculating machines, and also of the selectors and detectors which can scan data ten thousand times faster than can human beings. The significant results in radium therapy cannot be foretold, but the million volt X-ray tube, now used, bombards malignant cells with radiation equal to 95 million dollars worth of radium.

The old dream of the alchemists, transmutation of the

elements, has been realized through nuclear physics, atom-smashing, isotopes and artificial disintegration with atomic bullets. All energy phenomena are now conceived as being translatable one into the other; light, heat, sound, radio-waves, X-rays and "intangibles beyond" are thought of as aspects of wave-like movements of free particles through space, each class of phenomena having its own distinctive wave-length.

Important as these results are in physical and biological science, the most significant consequence is the interaction between neutron and uranium which causes nuclear fission (the explosive eruption of heavy atoms) to yield not only the smaller fragments of atoms but also the long envisioned goal of atomic energy. The far-reaching applications of this science give promise of changing human lives unendingly. We may yet be able to use the atomic energy of the sun directly without the roundabout service of green plants to which we owe all our present sources of energy: whether power—as steam, electricity or water; or fuel—as gas, wood, coal, oil or peat; or food—as sugars, starches, fats or proteins. Living is largely centered in sources of energy.

Atomic experts tell us that the fact that man can make atomic bombs does not mean that he understands atomic energy or the architecture of the atom. He has learned much about the behavior of protons, neutrons and electrons, but is now learning that these are always capable of change, one into the other, that they have neither permanence nor identity, that they may be composite. Nuclear physicists have subdivided the atom into 15 (some admit only 13) fundamental particles, and they are already wondering if these are actually the final stark, immutable and indivisible foundation stones of the universe.

These controversial matters are part of the order of nature which lies hidden beneath the manifest world of common experience. They point to the need for enlarging our understanding of the universe and of life.

Having briefly sketched our changed concept of the electrical structure of matter, we can now come back to our earth and its neighbors.

New discoveries lead to the probability that there are thousands of stars in our galaxy which may have inhabited planets. If only 0.01 per cent of all stars had planets, and only 1.01 per cent of these were earth-type, the possibilities of life, as we know it, existing on them are incalculable. Hoyle in *Nature of the Universe* (1951) writes: "I would say that rather more than a million stars in the Milky Way possess planets on which you might live without undue discomfort." [5]

For countless eons of its past, our earth must have been without life—from cosmic dust, through intense heat to condensation of its seas.

Earth's kind of life with all its amazing range of adaptations to various conditions could not exist on any other planet of our sun—not even on Mars, though some astronomers believe that it may possess its own kind of plants. Mercury always has its same side toward the sun so that one half is too hot for life, the other too cold. Venus lacks oxygen and has only carbon dioxide and ammonia. Freezing temperatures exist on Neptune. On Jupiter life would be simultaneously poisoned, frozen, asphyxiated and pressed upon by a million times terrestrial pressure; and so on with the others.

On stars themselves life could not exist, since they are so hot that atoms change their composition millions of times a second, and probably no two atoms ever stay joined together. Life's processes need some measure of duration in time.

Only after Earth's great heat had lessened and long-continued cooling had solidified its mass and condensed some of its encircling clouds into seas, could life have begun its adventurous undertaking, coming into being, maintaining itself, evolving new forms in the tepid oceans, then covering the emerging low continents with verdure; populating earth, air and sea with myriad creatures; and—most significant of all for us—bringing consciousness and mind and our questioning selves into being. Life and mind are Earth's unique contributions to the world we thus far know.

All the remarkable features of our earth are involved in its fitness for life as we know it; its dense crusted bulk with its advantageous distance from the sun; its size, which enables it to retain its atmosphere; its strange eccentricity of orbit which determines the inclination of the ecliptic; its relative amounts of solid, water and gas; these are all unique. We cannot yet be sure of such conditions elsewhere in our universe. It is quite obvious that earth's atmosphere has been an important determinant in the possibilities of earth's life.

How all the reciprocal conditions in the original order of nature arose no one knows. Our distinguished biochemist Henderson, in his notable early books *The Fitness of the Environment* and *The Order of Nature,* thinks there is not one

TABLE I

A TABLE GIVING SOME FACTS ABOUT EARTH'S ATMOSPHERE

1 TROPOSPHERE	16 lbs. to the square inch pressure at sea level; 80% of the weight of the atmosphere; 5 miles thick at poles, 10 miles at equator. Temperature falls about 1 degree for each 300 foot ascent; rapid changes, storms and calm, heat and cold, rain and snow.
2 TROPOPAUSE	A thin layer where temperature ceases to rise with increased altitude.
3 STRATOSPHERE	From 7 miles to 50. Planes can fly faster with less power and more safety but engines need superchargers to compress air to normal proportion of oxygen; cabins must be pressurized for people. Mild steady winds; sun's corona visible; stars day and night; ice crystal clouds sometimes appear.
OZONE LAYER of the stratosphere	Begins about 25 miles up in the stratosphere for about 40 miles; layers which absorb and hold heat; this warm air hastens movement of sound waves reflected from earth to ozone and back to earth as Marconi predicted and as gunfire demonstrates. Diffused ozone filters out extra ultraviolet rays which would destroy life on earth. Temperature recorded on thermometers on rocket ships loaded with instruments average 170°F at 40 miles dropping to 0°F at about 50 miles.
4 IONOSPHERE	These layers are of intimate importance to us because they reflect radio waves; some reflect longer, others shorter waves. An ion is a gas molecule which has been stripped of some of its electrons; it hunts around for others to take their place; the name means "traveler"; in this state they are fine conductors of electricity, and also act as electric mirrors to reflect radio waves.

chance in millions of millions that they arose by mere contingency, or chance. To some, the fitness of the setting suggests that earth's arrangement of substances and conditions was designed as a theater for life's performance. To some it has the look of a clearly defined plan—as if the drama had been anticipated, its setting and action directed—a biocentric earth. To others life seems the great actor and opportunist, growing, evolving, performing, making the most of whatever setting earth presents, a geocentric life. To another group the mutual fitness of life and its environment seems no more purposive nor purposeful than the decay of uranium into one type of lead. Both, they think, may be regarded as part of the machinery of nature. If conditions had not suited us, we should not be here.

In judging if direction or chance has determined these relations, we must avoid the kind of thinking exhibited by the tourist who exclaimed, "Isn't it wonderful how every big city has a great river at its front door?"

Out of the substances of earth with 92 elements, life uses only a few, 3 of the commonest and none of the rarest. There is no element peculiar to living things alone. Carbon, oxygen, hydrogen, nitrogen, sulphur and phosphorus, and a few others set together in certain definite ways and chiefly in colloidal (jelly-like) conditions, are the special and characteristic foundations of life. Living systems are indeed of the earth—earthy, fashioned from earth and fettered to earth by their composition from earth's elements and the conditions earth presents.

Four of the commonest elements used by living organisms —carbon, hydrogen, oxygen and nitrogen—differ from all others in their capacity to produce the widest variety of combinations and exchanges and in the great diversity of resulting chemical and physical properties. The chemistry of such carbon compounds is called organic chemistry, as contrasted with inorganic. Carbon is the only element in nature, except silicon in a lesser degree, which has the capacity of combining with itself to form rings or long chains of atoms. This makes possible and insures the formation of the very complex molecule of organic chemistry, a system made up of a great number of substances (indefinitely increasing), without which, life as we know it would be impossible.

While the relation of chemistry to life still presents many unsolved problems, the difficulties of solving them has not prevented great advances which have recently been made in integrating molecular chemistry and biological processes, such as the new agents of chemo-therapy: sulfanilamide and all its derivatives; penicillin, streptomycin, aureomycin; cortisone and many others.

Of all the substances used by living things, water is predominant in quantity. There are other relations of life and water determined by the conditions this compound of hydrogen and oxygen contributes to our planet. Water as a universal, inactive solvent is an active geological agent. A more chemically active one would be less durable because it would become saturated, and thereby no longer useful. It could then supply less rather than more of earth's chemicals to plants through their roots. Directly or indirectly plants are largely the source of the materials built into human bodies and into those of other animals and plants.

Water is the one substance which as vapor is a relatively

inert constituent of atmosphere (except as it causes weathering in rocks), an important and far-reaching feature in the meteorological cycle. No other liquid could pass through this cycle, binding so much heat in evaporation and giving up so much heat in condensation without sacrifice of some of the most vital features of present conditions.

Because of its high specific heat, surpassed only by hydrogen and ammonia, water serves as a great thermostat for earth's temperature, equalizing that of oceans, lakes and streams, tending to maintain their nearly constant temperature levels, moderating summer's heat and winter's cold. This modification of conditions is very important in the regulation of chemical processes of living creatures. Water conducts heat better than any other liquid, and its expansion when near freezing and when frozen is unique. If ice sank instead of floating at the surface, the depths of ocean, insulated from the atmosphere, would fill with ice affecting disastrous results on the temperature of the whole and therefore on the life processes of its inhabitants. Oceans influence winds, with resulting dissemination of moisture and distribution of rainfall. All these and other features are of utmost importance to plants and animals, and to the chemical processes essential to their living.

Because animal bodies average about 70 per cent water, a certain amount of outside heat has less effect on them than it otherwise would have, and the physiological, chemical processes which must go on within any living body are less disturbed by changes in temperature. But water is equally important in the detailed individual chemical processes of ionization and surface reactions within living cells.

Life undoubtedly came to our planet while it was entirely encircled by water. When lands were first lifted up, there were no land-living plants nor animals; but during the approximate 2 billion years since that happened, there have been profound changes.

The contours of our land are not primeval. Their history can be read and interpreted in the light of what geologists have learned about the constant forces which have worked upon them, sculpturing their surfaces and changing the outlines of the continents, which have had their ups and downs. Our landscapes have all had a past history. Some have come into being by catastrophic forces working on the crust of the earth, but most of them have become what they are by a slow process of atmospheric weathering and erosion on all exposed surfaces. Much of this material is transported by streams to the sea and accumulates along the borders of the continents, where under pressure and with the agency of cementing substances, it is consolidated into solid rock.

It is not surprising that these rocks, formed in water under such conditions, have preserved in them a record of the skeletal remains of the organisms of the seas under which they were formed. This storage process of an "at the time" roster of inhabitants of the seas, while successive layers of sediment were being bedded down, makes our planet's most important contribution to the evidence supporting the theory of evolution. The subsequent elevation, even into what are now mountains, is explained through the enormous forces which act upon the earth's crust.

The most significant fact about such sedimentary rocks

is their enormous total thickness which some geologists estimate to be not less than 25 miles. Such an accumulation under natural conditions must have taken an inconceivably long time, since all the processes involved in their formation are extremely slow; viz., atmospheric weathering, erosion, transportation of the material to the sea, deposition, consolidation by pressure, chemical action, and the final gradual elevation above the sea. The slowness of the deposition of limestones is better appreciated when it is realized that many of them such as chalk are formed by the shells of microscopic animals or the lime-encrusted coatings on such seaweeds as the corallines. Furthermore, it must not be forgotten that the sedimentary rocks are themselves subject to disintegration and decay under atmospheric action, and consequently undergo continual loss when exposed to weathering. Therefore, it is impossible to say how great the total thickness of sedimentary rocks may have been originally. At most, the sedimentary rocks exposed at the present time can be only a fraction of those formed and still forming under the sea, some of which have been raised above it.

Moreover, there is evidence that large areas of land have been raised above sea level and subsequently have eroded down to a gently rolling peneplain (such as that of southeastern New England at the present time), and at a later date have sunk again under the sea and have been covered with more sedimentary deposits, only to be raised once more above the sea—and so on through "cycles of erosion." The great impressiveness of the Grand Canyon of the Colorado in Arizona is due not only to its mile of depth as an example of erosion, but to the evidence in its North Wall of at least three cycles of erosion. In the light of such evidence we cannot doubt the great age of the earth.

Additional evidence on our planet's age comes from study of radioactivity of uranium rocks. These provide a precise method of measuring geologic time. The rate at which radioactivity takes place in rocks, together with the amount which has already taken place, indicates the length of time involved in attaining their present state. By critical checking, it is possible to determine what proportion of lead in a mineral is of radioactive origin, since the atomic weight of lead derived from uranium is slightly different from that of ordinary lead. When it was established that the comparative age of rocks may be measured by the time-clock of radiation, the Geological Society of America appointed a committee on the age of the earth. In 1928 it made its first report. The figure given from the evidence then available was 1 billion years. From later evidence, largely radioactivity research, the generally accepted figure of the report is 2 billion 500 million years.

Direct record of life extends back more than 1 billion years. Of this span of time, paleontologists believe they have a fairly complete record for the last 300 million years. This is chiefly taken from the sedimentary rocks where the material, often fragmentary or jumbled, has been sufficient to arrange a true sequence of living forms. These fossil forms are the basis of the evidence that a process of changes characterize plants and animals which have lived on our planet. Scientists agree they show descent with modification.

Early geologists had opened up this marvelous vista. The

vast series of ages, each inconceivably long, but each marked by its own characteristic forms of organisms, attested the capacity of living things to become increasingly complex. Fossils gave evidence that the more mobile and nervously complicated organisms like the vertebrates were comparatively late, while the simpler were in the earlier rocks. According to their antiquity as indicated by the age of their strata, each type, as we go back, differs more and more from its present-day living descendants. (See Table II)

The study of the basic life functions in existing organisms supports the view of Sherrington, England's most distinguished physiologist, Nobel Prize winner in 1932 for his work on *The Integrative Action of the Nervous System.* Sherrington writes: "Through asking how, modern science has come to know what life is—life is a chemico-physical system—nothing else. There is no boundary, no essential difference between the living and the non-living." Later in the same book, he writes, "Bethink you too that perhaps in knowing me (Nature) you do but know the instrument of a Purpose, the Tool of a Hand too large for your sight to compass. Try then to teach your sight to grow." [6]

Science and its progress are banishing from our lives the magic, mystery, and fear generated among primitive people by an untamed universe. Shall we let it banish also the recognition, appreciation, and faith resulting from the intuitions of mankind about the presence of a source of goodness, rightness, and purpose beyond themselves in our universe? Is there in our world something more than the nature with which science deals, namely a purpose to which the configuration of this nature of ours conforms?

TABLE II

	TIME UNITS	CHARACTERISTIC FEATURES
CENOZOIC ERA	Cenozoic Period Recent epoch	Modern races of men. Recent plants and animals. The stone age of human history.
	Pleistocene epoch beginning about 1,000,000 yrs. ago	Glaciation widespread. Mammals attain present heights.
	Pliocene epoch 13 million yrs. ago	Climate becomes cooler and drier. Man diverges from monkeys, gibbons and great apes.
	Miocene epoch 18 million yrs. ago	Mammals reach climax. Prairies spread and grazing types evolve. Elephants reach America.
	Oligocene epoch	Mammals evolve rapidly. Great apes arise in Eurasia.
	Eocene epoch	Modern orders of mammals arise and evolve rapidly.
	Paleocene epoch	Archaic mammals dominate. Valley glaciers exist locally.
MESOZOIC ERA	ending about 60,000,000 yrs ago Cretaceous Period 70,000,000	Dinosaurs, pterodactyls, toothed birds reach climax, then die out. Small early mammals appear. Bony fishes abundant. Flowering plants, hardwood forests spread widely.
	Jurassic Period	Dinosaurs and marine reptiles dominate. Toothed birds appear. Ammonites reach climax. Ganoid fishes.
	Triassic Period	Small dinosaurs and first mammals appear. Reptiles dominant. Ammonites evolve rapidly. Conifers and cycada dominate the forests.

TABLE II—*Continued*

	Permian Period 200,000,000	Continental uplift, mountains. Extreme dryness and cold result in rapid evolutions and many extinctions. Mammal-like reptiles.
	Pennsylvanian Period Carboniferous	Warm, damp climate helps coal-making. Reptiles and insects appear. Spore-bearing trees dominate swamp forests.
	Mississippian Period Carboniferous	Primitive amphibia and reptiles. Trilobites disappear. Shell-crushing sharks, lacy bryozoans, and crinoids reach climax.
PALEOZOIC ERA	Devonian Period 290,000,000	First forests. Lung-fishes evolve into air-breathing vertebrates. Amphibian foot prints. Brachiopods reach climax.
	Silurian Period	Armored fishes. Elasmobranchs. Climate warm, locally arid. Corals build widespread reefs. First land life.
	Ordovician Period 350,000,000	Seas widespread over low continents. Many new groups of invertebrates. First fishes, insects, vertebrates appear. Trilobites reach greatest differentiation.
	Cambrian Period 400,000,000	Fossils abundant for first time, representing marine life only. Plants recorded as lime-secreting algae only.
PROTEROZOIC EONS	500,000,000 years ago	
ARCHEOZOIC EONS	2,050,000,000 years ago	

CHAPTER TWO

Life and Its Activities

What is life? We know many facts about life and living things but find both difficult to define. The more we know, the harder it becomes to make a satisfactory definition.

We call the study of life and living plants and animals *Biology,* the science of life. But living organisms are so innumerable, so varied, so complex that knowing all their forms and activities and also all their reactions and relations to their environment is a field, in all its details, which no one mind can master. Biology is therefore divided not only into Zoology and Botany but into a very large group of life-sciences such as Embryology, Bacteriology, Cytology (study of the individual cell) and a long, long list of others.

There is no reason to believe that the activities and products of living organisms are mysterious. They are all made of atoms and the groupings of atoms of different elements which we call *molecules.* They exhibit electrical phenomena and work under the same laws that govern non-living air or rocks or stars. Science has banished much of the mystery of living things and has thereby increased the marvel of them and our sense of wonder.

The basis of modern biology is the conception that the changes and reactions that go on in living plants and animals are not fundamentally different from those which go on outside living things although they are *directed by conditions from within them.* Often overlooked, this factor of *self-direction* is of special interest to our inquiry.

On a bird walk one morning with a group of six-year-olds, a great plane flew over the meadow where we had been watching the flight of crows. As all eyes turned to follow its swift and noisy flight, I asked gently, "Does that plane seem to you more or less wonderful than a bird?"

"More," came the prompt reply, one voice ahead of the others. All the heads nodded assent.

"Can you tell me why?" I asked.

"It has a very wonderful engine," said the same eager voice still leading. The other slower heads again nodded agreement.

"But," I ventured, "if you had a plane that could start itself and steer itself and stop itself, could fill its own tank and keep itself oiled and greased, would you think it more or less wonderful than that plane?"

"I think I've made a mistake—a bird's more wonderful," said our spokesman, all the faces lighting up with approval.

Then, as we had earlier found a chipping sparrow's nest with three eggs, I asked, "And if your airplane could lay airplane eggs which would hatch out and grow—" I was interrupted with a glad shout! Life needed no further defense for those youngsters.

Living things carry on certain activities such as feeding, growing, breathing, getting rid of wastes, repairing, reproducing, and moving. Certain of these we can observe, but to understand them we need the facts and techniques of physics and chemistry as well as of biology.

Living always includes also the reaction of the organism to its surroundings, a constant adjustment and exchange with its environment. It is the element of direction of this exchange, its precision and orderliness, which makes the problems of the biologist so complicated and so challenging.

For example, the gallons of water that are known by experiment to pass from the leaves of a great elm tree into the surrounding air on every summer day are lifted to such heights and travel from the roots by the same forces as are utilized in any water supply system. The controls, however, are within the plants. No one turns faucets on and off. Guard-cells, at openings on the under sides of the leaves, open and close to determine the amount of moisture which can pass out. These react to conditions in the air, its temperature, humidity, movement, etc. Drought also affects their control through root pressure.

It is this factor of control by the organism which distinguishes a living system from one which is not alive. We have wonderful automatic machines, but they have their limitations. When a great loom stops instantly if a tiny thread breaks, it has to be started by an operator after the thread is mended.

Life exists in many forms, from invisible bacteria, single-celled protozoa, to giant trees and whales. They are all built of cells. The differences in size between a mouse and a man are due not to the size of the cells but to the number. Cells are usually microscopic, though they may be larger when stored with food. Within its cells is all the living substance that makes an organism alive. All the work involved in living is done by the substance in the cells called *protoplasm.*

If you watch a living cell under a high-power microscope, you see within the delicate, thin membrane of the cell wall, a fluid—protoplasm—moving and flowing. The motion is varied and continuous. You can recognize certain definite regions of the dynamic living whole. Nearly central is a somewhat spherical portion that appears more dense than the surrounding fluid. This central dense protoplasm is the cell *nucleus* and the surrounding less dense fluid, the *cytoplasm* (cell-plasm)—but both are protoplasm. All but a few types of cells, like bacteria, blood corpuscles, and some algae, have an easily identified nucleus.

A cell wall may be punctured and much of the cytoplasm taken out without killing the cell, which can make new cytoplasm. But if you remove or injure the nucleus, the results are serious. It cannot lose any part of its substance and survive. If the nucleus dies, the cell dies. The business of the cytoplasm is to select from blood or body fluids and to provide all materials that may be needed for the various processes carried on by the cells. *Direction* of these processes, not change in its constituent parts, is the work of the nucleus.

There is a limit to the amount of protoplasm which this directive nucleus with its specialized structure can control, so protoplasm is always in cells, usually microscopic, never in indefinite amounts as water or air or minerals or oil may be.

Each living cell is far more than the droplet of jelly-like protoplasm it appears. Each is the center of its own energy cycles. Each is a scene of oxidation, the release of energy and a series of links of ferment actions. Catalysts (substances that produce changes in other substances without themselves being permanently affected by the change) are ready in swarms and in trains, each to take its place in the thousand-linked chain of chemical action. The cytoplasm holds globules within globules of needed materials, each kind with its own qualities and potentialities. These are furnished from our food, changed in the cells of digestive organs and carried with oxygen by the blood to the fluids which bathe all cells. Hundreds of millions of the various shaped molecules of protein (like meat in their nature), suspended in fluid and bristling with chemical receivers, may be housed within the tiniest invisible cell. They do not merge together nor sink because each carries an electric charge. These charges repel each other.

Within each cell the nucleus, like any master builder, has its "blueprint" plan and can summon its outfit of enzymes (special catalysts) to bring the plan into being. A hundred or a thousand processes may go on within a living cell at the same time. Perhaps it takes a poet to quicken our minds to life's qualities.

LIFE

What am I, Life? A thing of watery salt
Held in cohension by unresting cells
Which work they know not why, which never halt;
Myself unwitting where their master dwells,
I do not bid them, yet they toil, they spin
A world which uses me as I use them.
Nor do I know which end or which begin,
Nor which to praise, which pamper, which condemn.
So, like a marvel in a marvel set,
I answer to the vast, as wave by wave,
The sea of air goes over, dry or wet,
Or the full moon comes swimming from her cave,
Or the great sun comes north; this myriad I
Tingles, not knowing how yet wondering why.[7]

Modern science has taught us to look upon our bodies as energy- and heat-producing engines, as chemical plants and as electric generators.

The cytoplasm of the living cell contains many chemical substances in its homogeneous fluid. They are in tiny globules, and globules within globules, which make it spongy and increase the inner surfaces, bristling with chemical receivers on which chemical reactions take place. As many as 34 elements have been identified in protoplasm, but the essential 16 are oxygen, hydrogen, nitrogen, carbon, sulphur, phosphorus, iron, calcium, potassium, magnesium, sodium, chlorine, with a trace each of copper, zinc, cobalt, and manganese.

No one has yet been able to take all these ingredients and mix them together in any way which will make them alive. Biochemists hope they may some day know enough to do it.

But at present all protoplasm is the product of living organisms and formed only in them.

Protoplasm and its products form the mass and structures of all living things, plants and animals.

Metabolism is the name given to the process whereby protoplasm converts nutrients into energy and tissues. The word comes from the Greek *meta* = between + *bole* = change. Protoplasm differs from all other matter in its ability to metabolize. It carries on the chemical changes by which energy is provided for the activities of all cells; by which materials are assimilated; by which assimilated materials are broken down (and sometimes even protoplasm itself) into their components; and by which are made new products and new protoplasm, the self-maintaining, self-building plants and animals.

In a complicated organism each cell does its part, each is an integrated energy system which depends for its upkeep on currents of energy passing through it. Nutrients as energy sources must flow in; waste with energy no longer usable must flow out. The cell wall is the medium through which the interchange between the cell's cytoplasm and its surroundings takes place. Fluids move freely through the walls by osmosis, but to some substances they are impermeable. There is undoubted selectivity of materials by the cells.

Life's activities as we know them would be impossible without protein, a nitrogenous carbon compound, the characteristic molecule in protoplasm. The word means *that which is first or prime.* Proteins are found in nature only as products of living cells, yet not all proteins are alive. When we consume and digest meats, fish, eggs, cheese, or milk, we are furnishing our bodies with the chief building materials. We must first break them down into their constituent amino acids and build them up again into hair, nails, skin, bones, muscles, blood, etc. Nature takes care of all these processes. It would do no good to swallow down amino acids, not difficult to find, to save the bother of cooking and eating. Nature seems to demand that we go through the process of breaking down proteins to build up new structures and repair old ones. This is the basic purpose of eating. To this process, nature has provided hunger and pleasure in food, including the joy of cooking.

Each group of related self-building organisms has its chemical individuality particularly in its proteins. There are probably special proteins for each genus of plants and animals. The work of the late Emil Fischer, Nobel Prize winner who first tried to piece proteins together, achieved the triumph of peptides. If we ever come to have synthetic beef steaks, it will be because he started chemists in the right direction. He showed inconceivable variety in the groupings and proportional representation of the nearly forty amino acids (some half of which are essentials) which make up in various linkages the complex protein molecules. He estimated that the number of possible proteins must be 128 followed by 25 zeros. To him this explained the infinite variety of plants and animals and also the difference between the protein in blood and the protein in milk, the difference between flesh and horn, silk and nerve. Woodward at Harvard thinks that Fischer was right.[8]

Proteins, though relatively stable, are continuously releasing their energy, breaking down into amino acids and being built up again by the activity of the enzymes in the nuclei of the cells, a part of the process of metabolism which includes all the chemical routine of living. More proteins are needed during periods of rapid growth and later after middle life when aging makes extra demands because of constant repairs. At such times the cytoplasm of cells should be supplied with food rich in protein.

But how did the vitally important mixture of earth's elements, the complicated, resourceful, infinitely varied and indispensable molecule of protein come to exist? Güye, the Swiss mathematician, is of the opinion that if the atoms of the universe were shaken together persistently so that nitrogen, carbon, sulphur, phosphorus and the other necessary elements fortuitously combined to form a single protein molecule of the simplest conceivable structure, 2 billion years would not be time enough to form such a molecule by chance. Yet living cells are so organized that they can build them constantly.

If you have watched crystals form on a cold window pane or in a liquid, you have recognized a degree of organization which seems higher than anything apparent in a liquid or gas where the molecules are rushing aimlessly about. In a saturated salt solution when the salt cubes form, each face with its central depression, an element of drill or regimentation seems to be present. This seems to be also true in the moisture of the air when it spreads its crystals in plant-like forms over your window glass or fashions the perfection of its snowflakes. The growth of crystals into larger and larger associations is accomplished by repeating the same structure in three directions over and over again without limit. The order of crystals is drawn from disorder!

But a very different and more complicated type of organization is observed in the living organism. Here every vital function is accompanied by an exchange of material whereby atoms are constantly taken up into and expelled from the organization which constitutes the living being. Nevertheless, its identity as an individual continues. Without benefit of science we can appreciate Walter de la Mare's way of putting it:

MISS T.

It's a very odd thing—
As odd as can be—
That whatever Miss T. eats
Turns into Miss T.;
Porridge and apples,
Mince, muffins, and mutton
Jam, junket, jumbles—
Not a rap, not a button
It matters; the moment
They're out of her plate,
Though shared by Miss Butcher
And sour Mr. Bate,
Tiny and cheerful,
And neat as can be,
Whatever Miss T. eats
Turns into Miss T.[9]

These living organized cells build the elements into themselves as they are needed in tissues, organs, and systems which carry on the growth and work of the organism, such as chlorophyll-cells, leaves, stems and roots in plants, or muscles, lungs, nervous systems, blood, etc. in animals. All the many varied structures are a result of the selectivity of cells, each governed by its nucleus in the self-building, living edifices of both plants and animals. Their orderly growth comes from order.

The factors in organization must synthesize, build and maintain the embryo, meantime establishing the cooperative unity of its millions of organized cells. These same factors must repair and sometimes replace damaged parts of the organisms. They must maintain constancy in each individual amid the give and take of selectivity, the equilibration of forces and materials needed for maintenance and growth. This refinement of organization is recognizable in many physiological processes.

Living organisms consist of parts which lose their essential character when once they are removed from connection with their wholes. The existence of one part of a machine does not depend on the existence of the other parts (though its usefulness may do so), but the life of each part of a living organism does depend on the life of the whole. It is a reciprocal relation. An organism is a dynamic system constituted of interdependent, unlike parts working together. Coordinative organization is as essential to its life as are its various structures and functions. However difficult the chemical phases of the origin of life and its maintenance are, the problem of the beginning of biological organization is far more complicated. It is difficult to think that any known principle of chemistry or of physics can explain the development of a definite form by an organism or a piece of an organism. When an egg develops into a chick, we are sure there was organization already in the egg to make it possible. All experiments such as Spemann's on regeneration of parts of injured animals, experiments on developing embryos and the experimental transplanting of cells from one region of the egg to another, face what seem insoluble problems in the forces of organizing relations in living cells.

In the complicated organism each cell does its share, but what binds them all into a cooperative unit? Even in human bodies, our conscious selves have no part in maintaining cell processes—beyond a few acts initiated by hunger or other discomfort such as a cramped position or close air in a room. What synchronizes all these processes giving unity and selfhood, what sustains the activity and identity of the individual complex of ever-changing substances amid never-ceasing variation in external conditions? Can the processes of chemistry and physics be so directive, so integrative, so synthetic? Or may there be some psychic factor as R. Lillie and others have speculated?

If you have been privileged to watch under a microscope the fertilization of star-fish or sea-urchin eggs in sea water, you have seen a sperm, little more than a self-propelled nucleus, enter an egg (many times larger than the sperm because of food-storage), and then have seen the living protoplasm of these two nuclei unite. With the union of these two nuclei a new life is initiated—a new organism begins its individual existence. These star-fish or sea-urchin eggs are similar both in appearance and in behavior (as is every kind of egg in its essential features), yet each united egg and sperm develops into the kind of creature from which the egg and the sperm came. Each fertilized egg cell with its new nucleus made by the joining of the two nuclei—one from the egg and one from the sperm—begins to divide and redivide; the one cell becomes two cells; the two, four; the four, eight; the eight, sixteen, continuing to double for a time. Although this is a process of multiplication through division, the cells do not separate. This is one of life's profound capacities. It can be seen under a microscope or in a moving micro-film, an act of creation taking place before your eyes like a slow dance, the factors moving harmoniously, as if to cosmic rhythms unheard by our dull ears.

The highly specialized intricacy of the nucleus can be further made visible under a microscope by using special stains. Then we can see chromatin (color material) which reacts strongly to basic stains, indicating a high degree of chemical specificity, while the other materials in the nucleus react weakly or not at all to these stains. In the nucleus of a resting cell, this granular chromatin is gathered in thread-like *chromosomes* (color bodies), coiled about irregularly, suggesting a network. But when a cell begins to divide, as it must for the processes of growth and differentiation, the chromosomes shorten and thicken into pairs, like packets, two of each different size and shape. These differences make it possible to trace their behavior during the process of division. The number of pairs, characteristic of different species, varies, but is constant throughout a specific group. Human beings have in the nucleus of each cell forty-eight chromosomes in twenty-four pairs, rabbits twenty-two pairs, mice twenty, fruit flies four.

This constancy in the number of chromosomes characteristic of each species supports the assumption that there is a causal relation between chromosomes and specific traits of the individual. Experimental evidence has established the presence of specific factors, called *genes,* which are the bearers of hereditary processes producing these traits. The pairs of chromosomes are organized into a mechanism whereby their *genes* are distributed to *every new cell formed in the body.* Each cell has a replica of this genetic system which regulates heredity. No one has ever seen a gene, but regions of them can be transplanted experimentally. They seem to be to life what atoms are to gas or minerals.

The division of the nucleus initiates this process which is called *mitosis* (from the Greek, meaning *thread*). It becomes less rounded, more thread-like as its contents flow toward either end to form two new centers. Each chromosome divides, and one of each duplicate moves toward one or the other of the two newly forming centers. Then the cell wall begins to constrict about the two new nuclei, and suddenly there are two cells in place of one, each with an exact replica of the nucleus which started the division and each cell capable of its own growth and activities.

Consecutive cell division brings about the growth of an organism. An egg becomes a chick. Except in the earlier rapid growth, it is not a frequent event in the life of a cell. The rate of division does not remain the same in all parts of the growing body, so the regularity of the numbers is broken. If you enjoy computation, you will find that fifty or sixty successive divisions will produce roughly the number of billions of cells estimated for a grown man. Meantime the cells are differentiating; what kind of a cell each becomes—a feather or part of an eye—is determined by the genes, a fact proved by experiments of transplanting regions of genes.

Another type of cell division takes place in germ cells in preparation for fertilization when an individual is mature enough to reproduce its kind. Both egg and sperm get rid of half their chromosomes. The process is called *meiosis* which means reduction. It is complicated, different in eggs and sperms, but it can be watched. Again, for our dull senses, there is no calling of the figures nor beat of cosmic rhythms. The beautiful intricacy and timing of the details of meiosis and the ingenuity of the experimental disclosure of its facts are a remarkable story worthy of the importance of its results—that in the union of an egg with a sperm the racial number of chromosomes in a nucleus shall not be doubled.

In all biparental germ cells, the paired chromosomes have come *one each* from the two parents. In this *reduction division* or *maturation,* preparatory to fertilization, the chromosomes do not *duplicate* by division, but instead, each pair *separates,* one of each going to one of the two newly forming centers of the dividing cell. It seems to be only chance that determines which one of the pair—one of maternal, the other of paternal origin—goes to which of the two newly forming centers. If, in this random process, one center receives more chromosomes of paternal origin, the other center has the reverse. But of these two new cells *one* is *discarded* and *disintegrates,* passing into oblivion; only one is destined to unite with a mate which has also undergone a reduction division. This union *restores* the *racial number* of *chromosomes.* But the proportional representation in the new cell of grandparent chromosomes, maternal and paternal, is unpredictable, as are all results of random processes. Because of this chance factor, there can be no duplication of individuals even among brothers and sisters, though there may be resemblance. Identical twins arise from a doubly nucleated egg or from an egg whose new mixture separates when it first divides, sharing the same nucleus.

Weismann was the first worker to establish the fact that the differences that set one individual apart from another are due to changes that had taken place in the germ cells from which the plant or animal had developed. With persistent experimentation he established his theory of the germ plasm: that germ cells are in no sense the product of the body which contains them, but are a direct part, early set aside, of the parental germ mixture which gave rise to the new individual in which they lie. This shifted the search for the causes of variation from the developed organism to its germ cells and their behavior, through the mechanisms they exhibit.

Since Weismann's day, the assumption of genes has been established. Genes have not been seen, but, like the assumption of invisible electrons in physics, they have been proved by experiments. There can be no doubt that in a cell nucleus there exist 2000 to 2500 genes (possibly many more), strung along bead-like in the chromosomes, each with an individual potency, different from every other, each taking its own part in the growth and development of every cell in each individual.

We must not forget that all cells in a complex animal or plant come by multiplication through division from one single fertilized egg cell and share its unique combination of chromosomes with their constituent genes. The forms of the adult cells vary as much as do the functions they perform, a diversity incredible in anything but living bodies.

It has long been known that the fate of a given piece of material in the developing egg depends to a certain extent upon its position in the whole. The fertilized egg is an organized whole. The potencies of the egg are due to the fact that the egg is the prospective organism, although its visible structure is that of a cell. There is danger of reaching wrong conclusions when we deal with the essential elements or constituents of the germ cells—nucleus, chromatin, genes, cytoplasm—independently and abstractly.

Perhaps you have watched a chick embryo when, after the egg's second day in an incubator, its heart is not only formed but functioning. On opening the shell you can see, in the small disk of cells on the surface of the yolk, the tiny embryo with its visible tubular heart beating regularly. If this whole is lifted from the yolk and kept bathed with normal salt solution, you can watch the heart beat, hastened by heat and retarded by cold, throughout a laboratory period.

We can partly understand how each cell formed from the fertilized egg cell may have an exact replica of that newly formed nucleus with its new combination of chromosomes and their constituent genes. But *differentiation* is directed by *identical* directive groups in each nucleus. One cell seems to know it must form muscle, another blood—one cell begins a hair, another a nerve. How may a *future need* be projected as a stimulus for *present* building? Does the selectivity of each cell result from *fore-knowledge* of its future function, enabling it to work to a plan? Is there evidence of design with each new-born cell finding and fulfilling its place in the pattern? We need to be shown that the processes of chemistry and physics alone are capable of such creative synthesis and integration.

It was a long but a direct step ahead when in 1905 and 1915 Albert Einstein's theory of relativity found that Newton's laws did not conform to reality, so that the assumption of the ether was swept away. Then Max Planck convinced his fellow physicists that light and radiation came not in ethereal waves but in packets which are called *quanta*. Quantum theory explains why the filament of an electric lamp gives light when it is heated by a current, and solves many related questions such as the principle of the photoelectric cell and other electronic problems.

Erwin Schrödinger, Nobel Prize winner (1933) in quantum theory, applies it to life processes which can turn an embryo into a man and use the directive genes in the chromosomes of the nucleus of each cell to produce the manifold tissues and organs which make up his organism. "We must," he says, "be prepared to find a new type of physical law prevailing in it." He does not call this new law non-physical nor super-physical but thinks it a "genuinely physical one"; it is, in his opinion "nothing else than the principle of quantum theory over again." He emphasizes the curious distribution of the hereditary substance in a many-celled organism as its mechanism of heredity and reminds us of "the fact that the single cog is not of coarse human make, but is the finest masterpiece ever achieved along the line of the Lord's quantum mechanics." [10]

Recent investigators of the nature of this essential unit of life, *the gene,* tend to take the position that it is an organic particle, probably a large protein molecule—the only thing we know that can organize protein molecules. Chemists know very complex structures which are organic molecules. Some protein molecules consist of thousands of atoms. The loss of a single atom might change such a molecule so that exact duplication would be stopped, blocking cell division and growth.

Geneticists are sure of three results of normal functioning of genes: that exact duplication takes place in the process; that the gene may sometimes mutate (change); that genes somehow control and pass on to the developing organism the various characteristics that distinguish it.

Variation through a new combination of genes is always secured through meiosis (reduction). Its random factor adds one more chance of securing newness. The greater the shuffling of genes the greater the chances for variation.

Every organ is re-created in each perfect individual; any identity between resemblances is based on the identity of the developmental processes producing them. These processes are interpreted by geneticists as being controlled by the hereditary units present by the thousands in the nuclei of all animal cells. These directive genes come equally from both parents and therefore are *doubled in variety of influence* but not in number. Each gene may affect the development of a number of structures in the new individual, or these structures may be influenced by a number of genes. Imperfections may occur. Dominance of one over the other is possible but unpredictable. When visiting relatives comment on your looks, the ready twinkle in your eyes so like your mother's father or the tilt of your nose so like your father's mother, be resigned. You can do nothing about your gene inheritance. Your task is to use it creatively.

By just such a union of genes, we know that the single fertilized egg-cell which started your life on its individual adventure became the billions of cells which now make up your body. This part of your biography is not imaginary, although no one observed it and you yourself were supremely unaware of it. It is known as a universal feature of life's beginning processes for all products of biparental reproduction. Every cell of your body has a replica of that first nucleus of yours and all the factors composing it, a genetic code mutual to all your cells, furnishing not only the plan of development but the strange power to direct the accomplishment of the plan in the development of the new individual—a new genetic mixture.

We have been describing the activities which go on in each individual organism to sustain its life processes. We need further also to consider the activities of variation and mutation which have such a significant relation to the origin of species and to the profound changes we call evolution.

The processes of variation and inheritance in one-celled animals are much simpler than in many-celled. Woodruff watched Paramecium, a one-celled protozoan, reproduce itself by fission (self-division) to the number of 9000 generations in thirteen and one-half years. Because the whole organism is in immediate contact with the physical and chemical conditions in the surroundings, any changes produced by environment in protozoa are directly shared in the development of the new individuals arising by fission (division). Jennings found that a favorable environment constantly increased the vigor, fission-rate, and variability of the resulting stocks, while adverse conditions were the exclusive factor bringing about degenerative changes. The loss of vitality and depression were inherited and continued long after conditions had been changed for the better. Also, vigor and size inherited were lost very slowly after conditions became unfavorable.

Conjugation (union) in unicellular organisms assures occasional biparental reproduction and is a source of variations. Protozoa may unite temporarily in conjugation, exchange parts of their nuclei, then separate and continue reproduction by fission, initiated always by division of the nucleus. Members of a uniform stock after conjugation produce descendant races and stocks differing in inherited characteristics, such as size and vigor, rate of multiplication and resistance. It is clear that the nucleus contains materials which affect deeply the development and characteristics of each individual, as is true in higher organisms.

This matter creates great interest and an active field of experimentation not only because geneticists are still searching for an unknown factor in evolution that will explain adaptive variations and their inheritance, but also because at times in a process called *synapsis* in the nuclei of germcells, large groups of genes are exchanged by homologous chromosomes as a result of "crossing over." This partial mingling of the substances of two chromosomes suggests a secured means of obtaining new mixtures with increased vigor for variation.

In multicellular organisms there is no way in which the

germ-cells of an individual may be changed after they are formed. No changes in the environment can affect their nature. There is no mechanism whereby changes in the body or the mind of an individual, adaptive or otherwise, could produce any changes in its germ-cells. No educational skills, no mutilation of parents, or other acquired characteristics can be transmitted to germ-cells and thereby inherited.

Changes in the nature of germ-cells while they are being formed are therefore responsible for all inherited variations. They are an unfailing feature of hereditary processes and thus are an important factor in evolution.

If evolution has taken place by the transformation of one species into another, both in plants and animals, there have been variations and they have been inherited, passed on from one generation to another. For most scientists the premises of the theory of evolution are now accepted as established facts. Divergence through variation goes on all the time, even within a given species. It is the basic means of producing diversification in the forms of organisms. These branchings indicate proportional differences in the stock of hereditary units.

Mutations (from the Latin *to change*) are discontinuous variations, the extremes of which are not connected by intermediates. Examples are more familiar in hybrid plants (such as evening primroses) than in animals, where hornless cattle, Manx cats, six-toed cats, and some distinctive breeds of cattle, poultry and pigeons are results of mutations. Mutations were earlier called "sports." They are not always conspicuous variations, but they are *heritable,* always breeding true to form from the first, which indicates that the change producing the mutation was some *change* in the *germ-cells.* This gives *mutations,* whatever their cause, a direct leverage on evolution. Some geneticists think them more important than new combinations.

Mutations are sometimes harmful, and, because of the character of the change or the loss of a gene, may produce some hereditary defect. Sometimes a mutation may change a gene in such a way that it brings about a useful variation in the body, but at present mutations are considered as rarely *adaptive,* i.e. adding to efficiency.

Mutations occur in nature. They have never been understood nor explained. Laboratory experimentation, however, has been able to *induce* mutations.

The best material for this study has been the very large and transparent cells of the salivary glands of fruit flies. This material had also the great advantage of having only eight chromosomes (four pairs) in each of its cells. But its greatest asset was the ease of breeding and feeding the flies, and the rapid rate at which they produce new generations. In nine days your answer to some problem of the inheritance of a mutation would be forthcoming.

When Morgan and his school had bred flies by the millions, keeping records of the pedigree of each, they found out of 20 million flies 400 mutants that bred true. Four hundred new species were recorded in thirty years. But most of the mutations seem slight and unimportant. No large, discontinuous steps appeared. No great novelties were produced.

Experiments to try to change genes—by *mutation,* by removal of certain regions of chromosomes, by the use of colchicine, drugs, poisons, alcohol, anaesthetics, whirling, shaking, heat and cold, light and darkness, starvation and over-feeding—followed in quick succession, but the genes were not easily jolted out of their accustomed ways.

Taking suggestions from nuclear physics, experiments were tried on the effect of radiation on genes. X-ray, radium, ultra-violet light, pitchblende and other radioactive materials were used. The results were immediate and astonishing. Instead of the former proportion of mutants, Muller had 150 times as many, some of them so modified that they qualified as new species, and they bred true—legless flies, wingless flies, flies with red eyes, some covered by hair, some naked, all strangely unlike their parents and unlike those not exposed to X-rays or the other sources of radiation. No one knows clearly just what happened. The constitution of the genes may have been changed or they may have been shifted in position, but new species arose and persisted, breeding true to type.

Just what causes mutations outside of laboratories is not yet known. It has been suggested that cosmic rays with their terrific bombardment of atomic structures both inside and outside of organisms may be responsible for mutations, but no proof is yet available. The field of induced mutations is under active experimentation at present.

Changes occur in genes as mutations. These give rise to changes in the structures directed by the genes in the nucleus. If the changes are slight, the results are inconspicuous: the organ or the individual will not differ widely from its predecessor. But if they are great, with many genes involved, the organ affected, or even the individual, may differ obviously from its parents.

Induced mutations show no tendency to be oriented, to be adaptive, or to be important. Some are harmful, some are fatal; no acquired characteristics have any influence on the nature of mutations.

Modern studies of mutations have established the fact that evolutionary development of new bodily characters may occur in the face of or at least independently of any direct influence in environment. We cannot therefore regard evolution as a mere result of action and reaction between the physico-chemical factors of environment and those of a passive, or possibly neutral organism. There seems to be a dynamic factor.

If like variations occur in lines of any group of organisms in different parts of the world, we need no longer assume that they have spread from a common center. We have been shown that they may have come from parallel mutations.

A mutation is a definite change in hereditary treasure which can only come about by means of some change in the hereditary substance. Before the rediscovery of Mendelism, deVries, a Dutch botanist, had recorded the sudden and random appearance of new varieties of his evening primroses, which we now know came from chromosome aberration. He published his generalized *Mutation Theory* in 1901 because he thought that in it was a new and effective factor in evolution.

Since quantum theory was only two years old when this happened, we have but slowly come to think of mutations as explained by quantum theory of the physicists, with no intermediate energies occurring between two neighboring energy levels—quantum jumps in the gene molecule.

Chromosome molecules doubtless represent the highest degree of well-ordered atomic association we know of in our universe. This is possible because of the individual role every atom and every radical is playing in it. Only such molecules, with their existing order, could maintain themselves and produce orderly events in growth and differentiation. Such elaborate protein molecules have been known to *reproduce themselves.*

Quickened by the agitation over the theory of evolution, all far-seeing biologists were puzzling over the problem, "How is the extraordinary multiplicity of living forms to be explained?" The permanence of every variety seemed firmly entrenched against any theory of progressive evolution. But experimentation was in the air. Nature was giving answers to some questions which were asked by carefully controlled experiment.

Mendel's work in crossing different species of plants, done in a monastery garden, was a response to this new spirit of inquiry through experiment that was stirring all over Europe. When in 1866 he gave his first papers, their significance was not appreciated. He was talking about things which could not be *seen* but were *indicated by results.* His main assumption was that the living individual might be composed of distinct hereditary factors.

Years after, Rutherford postulated that the structure of atoms explained their observed behavior in radioactive substances. His assumption was later proved true by tests and new techniques and by the amazing development of the science of electronics. So also Mendel's assumption about distinct hereditary units (now called genes) as well as the bodily mechanism for their *distribution* and *combination* were afterward proved true by microscopic observation and the rapid growth of the science of genetics.

Genetics can not yet explain *why* the chromosomes (which carry the genes) of the father and the mother should divide so invariably that some features of the father and some of the mother are passed on to each child. Nor does it explain why sex-linked traits like color blindness and hemophilia while carried by daughters appear only in sons.

Quantum theory, which explains why atoms in an electric light filament give off light when they are heated by a current, has been applied to photoelectric cells and television but is just beginning to illuminate the problem of physiology as in Schrödinger's application of them to gene activities.

When death comes to an organism, its catalysts no longer build and build to a plan; they tear down. The lifeless organism continues for a time to show its living characteristics of mass, spacial relations, weight, form and structure, both in the large and in detail, but the endurance of this structure fails. Its resistance to disintegrating forces is gone. The decay of equilibrium has come with death; its processes are irreversible. What has gone from this dynamic entity—what has become of its stability, that strange constancy, that extraordinary quality of individuality and its continuing identity? Is it for you an adequate analogy to say, "If you substitute oil for acid in the battery of your car, no current will pass?"

Whether life's "currents" are wholly chemicophysical, or the process of chemistry and of physics *plus* something else, it has long been known that many biochemical properties of the cell are intimately associated with the integrity of its structure; once that is destroyed they are destroyed too. The minimal freedom we must allow an organism in order to keep it alive is just large enough to permit it, perhaps, to hide its ultimate secrets from us. Therefore it is difficult to find out how tissues and organs work within the body. But removal from the body, while it makes an end of most life processes, makes available structural details and some facts of chemical composition. Microscopic examination furnishes a static picture of the form each cell has built to carry on its functions and also reveals how it has disposed the materials selected by it to form tissues and organs. What is the basis of this accurately placed selectivity of living cells, this seemingly intelligent building as if to an agreed-on plan to fit a definite usefulness?

Is there an organizing principle specific to developing organisms and immanent in the organization of matter itself? Biochemists ask that this coordinative working to a plan be taken, not as a postulate (something given), but as a problem. They think it better to try stretching our concepts of physical and chemical processes than to abandon them because they fail to explain this inscrutable problem. We know what occurs but we cannot understand as yet *how it can occur*.

Theoretical phases of biology are slow in making progress partly because of inherent difficulties, partly because they have seemed "up in the air" to practical biologists and experimental workers, pressed as they are by the varied and difficult problems opening up on every side. Physics meantime made its unprecedented advances because of its frank recognition of the value of purely theoretical aspects and its wide explorations on these fronts.

The central problem of theoretical biology today, and doubtless for many a day to come, is organization. Whence comes this creative synthesis, this regulative, integrative organization in living systems? Is organization an elemental, universal property or capacity present in the stuff of the world from the beginning? Is organization *everywhere* present in matter-energy as Whitehead thinks, or only in the *somewhere* of living organisms?

Is the behavior of planetary electrons in the atom and of celestial bodies in our solar system a result of organization? While opinions may differ on this question, all scientists agree that the living world has units involving a far higher degree of intrinsic organization than any units of the nonliving world. The source and significance of organization in living things is part of our quest.

CHAPTER THREE

The Evolution of Life

When and where and how did life come to exist on our lifeless planet? No one really knows, though there is strong evidence that life began in the earth's oceans before sunlight penetrated the encircling clouds and before any land had been lifted above the waters. While any theory about the beginning of life must be a guess, the questioning does something to clarify the thought of the questioner. Can you think that life arose by mere chance, as expressed in that grandiose phrase, "a fortuitous concourse of atoms"? Did life "just come"? Can you believe it a result of spontaneous generation?

The work of Pasteur has established in modern thought the fact that life as we know it, both seen and unseen, comes only from previous life. But in the beginning? We know of no cosmic source of pre-existent life from which earth's life could stem. Does the presence of living organisms on a planet which had earlier been unfit for life imply for you the work of a creator? Was life created, in the sense of bringing something into being out of nothing? Or was there a method familiar to us through human creativity, a technique of using materials at hand under conditions already existing—resident forces? Either might involve something synthetically creative at the center of the world—some factor within the integrative organization of living systems which might explain life's start and evolution. Since there are no answers of fact to these questions, science dismisses them, not as unimportant, but as beyond its method. Yet scientists keep on experimenting.

Vitalists have held that the appearance of life on our planet involved a new force. Some thought of it as a creative factor from outside. Others considered the factor as imminent in the nature of matter-energy, coming from within. Mechanists dismissed it as part of the machinery of nature, something given. The protoplasm of living things is made from lifeless elements. The process of its making goes on within our own bodies all the time, and in all the plants and animals about us. But on a lifeless planet there must have been a beginning when matter-energy became living. Are we to think of it as creation or as transformation or as transition? Biochemists tell us that as a transition it is thinkable only if it is considered *at root* as a matter of chemical rearrangement. They cannot regard it as a transition from one fundamental category to another fundamentally different one. But it is easier by far to accept rearrangement of materials as a cause of life than to find out what caused the first rearrangement—that change in the relations of earth's materials which produced the first stirrings of life. No one knows how or why life began, but some speculative thought may quicken our minds to the details of the problem.

Was it in some tumultuous cataclysm that the first transition from lifeless to living material attained this rearrangement, trembling into being to become the base of all earth's significant life? Or were there multiple birthplaces for this far-reaching event on our planet? Did a creator or sun's heat or cosmic rays or some wandering chemical or a strengthening ferment or an enzyme or sudden electrical charge lift the first lifeless material into a living system—into some semblance of the colloid, dynamic micro-organism which today we call a living cell? No experiment has shown us as yet, and we may never know. Whatever the power or the forces causing that first transition from lifeless materials to living systems, as far as we know, only cells that are alive possess such alchemy today.

Biologists know enough about life and its requirements to have kept living tissues removed from the body of a chick, alive and growing in nutrient fluids for over fifty years (far longer than such tissues were likely to survive had they been left intact in the body of the chick); but no new starting-point for a new individual has been found except an already existing life. Each new individual starts as a division or as a bud from an already existent life—a detachment of a new life from a previous life. Like the treasured coals of our ancestors, cherished from hearthfire to hearthfire to kindle anew the glow of living flame, these detachments may make a new self, itself and no other, a new one, and only one, of the billions of portions of living-systems of the world—a new venture in the old process of living.

Life's first forms had to be self-sustaining with only inorganic sources of energy as food to build into living protoplasm. They must have been both complex and unstable but dynamically balanced, with governing systems as part of their constitution to regulate their balance. Life was a builder, the first maker of proteins, the nitrogenous carbon compound which forms the essential substance of all living things, the protoplasm which does the building, and of which nuclei are so largely built.

Can you regard matter-energy as having had in it from the beginning not only sub-atomic and sub-molecular organization but also the latent capacity of producing the world of living energy-systems whenever the conditions were right? When the mushrooms of a fairy-ring appear on your lawn over night, without earlier evidence of their presence or readiness to fruit, you infer that the unseen part of the growth had been perfected. In the same sense the appearance of life may have been a fruition of organizing relations present from the beginning in the stuff of the world, waiting to take on life's processes whenever conditions made it possible. How and why the stuff of the world came to be that way is another question, always coming back to thoughtful minds.

Returning one morning from a collecting trip in a swamp with a nine-year-old boy, I asked, "How would you like to take this pitcher-plant and try to find out how many kinds of insects it has caught?"

Wistfully he answered, "What I'd really like to try to find out is *how it came to be that way*."

Before life appeared, the structure of atoms and of molecules was doubtless much as it is today. These show organization and capacities for combining, but in too simple a stage to call *alive*. Atoms unite to form molecules of simple compounds such as water, carbon dioxide and salt. Molecules may unite with others to form more complicated compounds such as sugars, starches and fats, and substances called catalysts and enzymes. Enzymes are a special class of catalysts which can synthesize proteins from simple amino acids, or glycogen from simple carbohydrates. The turning point of lifeless materials into living protoplasm may have been reached by a protein-building enzyme whose presence was selective, assembling, organizing. Some biochemists think that the chance organization of a complex carbon-containing molecule, whose presence induced the synthesis of other units like itself, might occur because of carbon's tendency to form long chains of its atoms. This in its essence might be considered alive. Or the pattern of energies which brought about the first living molecules may easily have been a unique pattern.

Horowitz in his *Evolution of Biochemical Synthesis,* suggests that the first form of life was a "protogene" which chanced by a basic chemical grouping into an organization capable of reproducing itself as viruses do, and of mutating and slowly developing by changes into something truly alive. More recent studies of gene activities as an organic particle and of experiments with biochemical synthesis are full of interest and promise. They may yet solve the problem of the chemical synthesis of life.

Was it when earth's fog-wrappings lessened and sunlight could penetrate her atmosphere that the *miracle-worker chlorophyll* appeared? Possessing this, the green plant uses part of the energy of sunlight to take carbon from carbon-dioxide to build its carbon compounds in one of the most basic processes of all nature. Green plants are great growers and builders. On their capacity to synthesize substances from earth, air and water into food for living systems depends not only the verdure which covers our continents but also the life of all animals. No organism without chlorophyll (except the autotrophic bacteria) can build its protoplasm, containing proteins and carbon compounds, directly from nature's elements. Animals must remake theirs from those built up by plants, as do our dairy animals; or use other animals as food, as we use beef, lamb, pork, poultry, fish, and life's products—eggs and milk. This is the supreme contribution of plants and their chlorophyll to the existence of life and its evolution.

Each plant is a builder, not only of sugars, starches and fats, but also a maker of proteins—the nitrogenous carbon compound, the characteristic feature of protoplasm. Protein is the essential substance for maintaining life. Early in life's history as now, it is found in nature only as a product of living cells; then as now, it is the mixture of materials which does the building, and out of which the living formative parts of living systems are largely built.

Just when or how or why animal cells dependent on the work of plants came into being, we cannot know. Biochemists tell us that they know no chemical reason why all living things should contain glucose; but a *common ancestry* for *plants* and *animals* is the only explanation they can give, that it is always dextro-rotary glucose and never the other form, its mirror image.

The basic difference between plants and animals lies in their command of energy sources. Animals, always food users, lacking chlorophyll and being unable to make their own food, appropriated the materials produced by plants as a source of already lifted energy. Eventually some of them came to profit by using other animals or their eggs or milk as food. These yield a still higher source of energy. Both plants and animals are thus users of borrowed energy and of torn down materials. Life sets its course against the tide, and sails into the adverse winds of diminishing energy.

Life solved the problem of its sustenance, its continuity and its perpetuation on earth, by winding itself up, and chlorophyll was its magical key! Green plants could transform energy from a less to a more available form. The results of this energy could accumulate beyond the needs of the moment. Life could evolve.

The theory of evolution has had a long and stormy history in modern thought. It implies the descent of widely different forms of life from a few elemental kinds in a remote past! Only the simplest life-forms are found in the oldest fossil-bearing rocks. When more and more fossils began giving evidence of descent with modification, biologists all over Europe started puzzling over the problem of explaining the multiplicity of kinds of living forms. Certainly like came from like; offspring resembled their parents or grandparents. Yet it became apparent that each year gardeners and stock breeders were reaping rewards from new varieties of seeds and careful selection of cattle, pigs, and horses.

In rationalistic France, even before the publication of Darwin's *Origin of Species,* the idea of evolution had been stirring for some time. Lamarck (1744-1829) had stated the first general scientific theory of evolution. He held evolution to be a general fact which includes every form of life in a simple historical process. He based it on an ancient and non-evolutionary conception of living organisms occurring in a sequence from less to more perfect forms which he combined with a belief that change involves progress. He did not fail to note, however, the exceptions and disturbances which took place. More than many later proponents of evolution, he observed that the two factors of direction and orientation were accompanied by chance and random features and he insisted that both must be explained in a consistent general theory. He emphasized adaptation through use and disuse of organs, but he assumed the inheritance of *acquired* characters induced by habits and environment. Modern experimentation has refuted this assumption.

In England, Darwin was chosen to go as naturalist on the voyage of H.M.S. Beagle. While in South America he was puzzled by his observations of the strange resemblance between the giant fossil animals, whose remains he dug from the more recently formed rocks, and the little armour-plated armadillos he found still living in the region.

After Darwin finished his report for the five-year Beagle expedition, he gave himself to sifting his observations and to gathering new ones, studying the methods used by breeders to produce new varieties of domestic animals. He clearly saw that the chances of promoting improvements were increased by a breeder who would select animals which varied in a desired direction. From this observation he made the deduction that somewhere in nature was an unknown selector or breeder. This gave birth to his idea of natural selection as the means whereby evolution had been brought about. This assumption in Darwin's first formulation has not withstood the test of time. Natural selection is still a factor in evolution but does not depend on existence or survival as applied to individuals or even to populations or species. Working through differential reproduction, its relation to the best-adapted is relative and approximate, not absolute.

Darwin felt impelled in the face of his mass of evidence to replace a belief in special creation by a belief in evolution. In the last paragraph of his introduction to *Origin of Species* he wrote:

> Although much remains obscure and will long remain obscure, I can entertain no doubt after the most deliberate study and dispassionate judgment of which I am capable, that the view which most naturalists until recently entertained and which I formerly entertained—namely that each species has been independently created—is erroneous. I am firmly convinced that species are not immutable.

Then in 1859 like a thunderbolt, came Darwin's *Origin of Species* to disturb the quiet air of accepted and traditional thought. The first edition (1250 copies) was exhausted on the day of publication. Simpson in *Landmarks in the Struggle between Science and Religion* writes:

> It was eagerly devoured, and while it excited in the minds of the younger students delight and enthusiasm, it aroused among the older naturalists anything from cool aversion to violent opposition.
>
> The attitude of the religious world toward this book is well illustrated by the remark addressed to Canon J. M. Wilson by his father, a country clergyman, to whom young Wilson, then a master at Rugby, had taken a copy of Darwin's book as a Christmas gift in 1859, one month after

its publication. "I cannot conceive," said the old gentleman to his son, "how a book *can* be written on the subject. We know all there is to be known about it. God created plants, animals, and man out of the ground." [11]

In *Darwin and the Origin of Species,* Sir Arthur Keith says of Darwin:

> He knew he was treading on dangerous ground; for an Englishman to doubt the truth of the Biblical record in the year 1857 was to risk becoming a social outcast; but, for Darwin, to run away from truth was to be condemned by a tender conscience as a moral coward. He was a sensitive man, reflective, quiet, warmhearted, ever heeding the sensibilities of his friends. Added to this he was also intensely modest and as intensely honest, fearing above all things even the semblance of a lie in thought or in act.[12]

What Darwin thought about the possible effect of his work of twenty years of fact-gathering on the established religious thought of his day is perhaps indicated in his concluding paragraph of the *Origin of Species:*

> There is grandeur in this view of life, with its several powers, having been originally breathed by the Creator into a few forms or into one; and that whilst this planet has gone cycling on according to the fixed law of gravity, from so simple a beginning endless forms most beautiful and most wonderful have been and are being evolved.

Few thinkers of today consider this statement irreligious. Here is the modern religious conception of Creative Mind continuously at work in the world-process, inexhaustible in its activity. Eddington in *The Nature of the Physical World* puts it, "Not once in the dim past, but continuously by conscious mind is the miracle of creation wrought."

It is difficult for us today to realize how unprepared men's minds were for any such account of *creative forces still at work* as were presented in Darwin's *Origin of Species.* The Bible and Milton's seventeenth century imagery were the accepted authorities for the process of creation. When in 1844 the only book preceding Darwin's *Origin of Species* (1859) which gave a full exposition of evolutionary views was published in Great Britain, it came out anonymously. Accounts tell us it was discussed only in whispers and the author's name withheld, to become known only through a contributed introduction to the *twelfth edition* (1884) which came out thirteen years after the author's death in 1871.[13]

We must recognize that the theory of evolution did not arrive as a great dome of light under whose truth all facts could be illuminated and could have their relationships revealed. Like most innovations in ideas, it had a bitter conflict to wage, not only against established beliefs but against the always-present lag in human willingness to accept new ideas when readjustment is required. The acceptance of evolution as a fact based on undoubted evidence is one of the most revolutionary changes ever brought about in the history of thought.

If we follow some of the steps taken by living things in their long history, we may find clues to trends and capacities which are significant in helping to decide the question of directive or chance in evolution. Perhaps both work together as they do in heredity and variation.

Botanists claim that the first forms of life were plants, microscopic aquatic bacteria—not the parasitic forms that now cause diseases, but a kind called autotrophs which live by oxidizing iron, sulphur, methane gas, carbon monoxide, or hydrogen.

One kind which is found in our mineral springs today lives by oxidizing iron. It is slimy, and only when you get it under a microscope can you believe that it is a living organism. The walls of the filaments are of iron, deposited by accretion around living bacterial cells, somewhat the shape of tadpoles. Inside their iron filaments, clear cut and definite such as only living things could build, they divide by fission in endless succession. They must have existed in unimaginable numbers for countless ages in the iron-charged waters that once overlaid the oldest rocks, if as is thought by some, the ooze they formed has now become iron ore.

Another type of these autotrophic bacteria lives by oxidizing sulphur. It is sometimes planted in septic tanks by sanitary engineers as an effective destroyer. In soil, its prime usefulness depends on its production of sulphuric acid, the only form in which with lime (sulphates) it can be absorbed from soils by the roots of plants and supply the sulphur which every living cell must have for its nucleus.

Another group of autotrophs is important because it contains pigments (not chlorophyll which gives the green coloring to plants, but red or purple from the dark end of the spectrum), the only light available in a cloud-enveloped world. Surviving forms of this kind die at once if exposed to free oxygen; in dim light they live and carry on *photosynthesis*. These are considered pioneers in the process of food production because of their use of the energy of light. Until this pigment mechanism appeared, *chemosynthesis* had furnished the energy needed for food production in autotrophs.

Another pioneer in using light photosynthesis was the group of blue-green algae which flourished in the watery world before sunlight could penetrate the heavy clouds overhanging earth's tepid, all-encircling oceans. We can find them today in ponds and stagnant waters, smelly and offensive. If the gelatine tubes they secrete are removed, the plants die at once, killed without this protection by the very light they live by.

Next (the botanists claim) came green algae with chlorophyll, so like in its composition to the red coloring of our blood. The green color may in some algae be obscured by the addition of brown or red pigments, but chlorophyll works even when somewhat hidden. Life was doubtless entirely water-living when this miracle-worker appeared, the action of which is basic.

The simplest animals, and probably the earliest ones to exist, are called protozoa. They are microscopic, chiefly aquatic creatures which in the most primitive way carry on each in its one cell all the essential activities of living animals, such as breathing, feeding, moving, feeling, getting rid of wastes, and reproducing. There are still thousands of kinds of them living in water and sometimes as parasites in other living organisms. The greatest number and variety of kinds are found on the surface of the seas where they feed on one-celled plants and fragments of others and upon each other, and where they provide the basic food for all sea creatures.

Two groups of protozoa have left shells as long-lasting evidence of their presence. In one group these are made of lime, and in the other of silica. These microscopic shells have a great variety of shapes and patterns in the various species, some with perfect symmetry and great beauty. Almost twice as many shell-bearing fossil forms are known as there are living kinds today. The ancestors of these can be traced far back into geologic time. Large areas of the bottom of the Atlantic Ocean are known to be covered by an ooze made chiefly from such limey shells. In many parts of the world thick rock strata have been formed from them and lifted up, as were the chalk cliffs of England and also those in nearby France, in Kansas, now so far from the ocean, as well as in Greece, still nearly surrounded by the sea.

The silica-shelled protozoa still exist abundantly in tropic and temperate waters. Rocks made of their ancestral fossil remains have been raised above the sea in such widely separated regions as Sicily and the Barbados.

During the long period while life was entirely water-living, plants and animals had become multicellular. Cells that could divide without separating, that could multiply and stay together, were the explorers which added this resource to life's activities. By this path, division of labor entered the evolutionary process. Cells that were freed from carrying on all of life's processes for themselves could now specialize. Each multicellular organism had multiple needs and multiple ways of meeting them. While the life of each cell was simplified, the life of the whole living organism was made more complicated. New organization had come into being to balance, to unify, to regulate and to integrate all the increasingly complex processes which each cell had once carried on. This too made for evolutionary progress.

All the one-celled organisms increase by fission, a division process which endlessly multiplies the old individual whatever its qualities. This is a perfectly successful method of reproduction. But some of the giant algae which had developed hold-fasts, anchoring them to one spot permanently, developed spore cases filled with spores. Each spore was a potential individual like the parent. It could be released to develop later independently, without loss of identity of the parent plant. This too was also an adequate method of reproduction as far as numbers were concerned.

But the green algae, their chlorophyll well established in both structure and function, developed two different kinds of reproductive cells which had to unite to form a new individual. Present-day experiments have shown that the union of two strains of protoplasm tends to produce new qualities and new vigor in both plants and animals. The Age of Seaweeds followed the development of this method of reproduction in the green algae. The increased, luxuriant growth may have been partially due to the innovation in the reproductive mechanism. It proved a forward step for evolution.

The lime-secreting algae were laying down deposits, building up the rocks in swirls and bosses, plates and knobs, blanketing the submerged continents with what has now become limestone. When the Rockies were thrust up, such fossil-bearing limestones were lifted two miles into the air. They are also buried deep under the present cornfields of Illinois. Sixteen times, the seas are known to have come and gone from the plains of that region, alternating with the fern forests and the great spore-bearing trees which left their fossil records in the soft coal deposits of that land. The ground-pines in our woods today are collateral descendants of a tree that grew in the coal age a hundred feet high with a stem four feet thick. It was an age of spores, millions of them in one spore case, billions of them from one tree, now preserved in the coal partially made from them.

Most of the phyla of invertebrates existing today are represented in the fossils found in the sedimentary stratified rocks of this spore-bearing period. Few have become extinct. Each phylum represents a distinctive plan of structure and function which each line of varying descendants has kept in diverse detail. The oceans teemed with the soft-bodied marine forms whose skeletal remains have left such rich records. Fossils have testified not only to the large numbers existing but also to the waxing and waning of such numbers and to the changing proportions in any given population. They have taught us that new species do not take the place of ancestral forms but are coexistent with them for prolonged periods, and only sometimes become dominant or extinct. They have shown us that mutations appear suddenly but tend to be repeated in various centers.

It is important to consider some of the more momentous steps taken on the long, branching, and at first watery road followed by the successive ancestors of the human species in their ascent toward man. To sketch these, however briefly, is futile unless it helps us to understand man's place in nature, his position in the world of life and his relation to other living things during the process of his making.

Through a long period of time, which is life's most unlimited resource, the action of man's creation moves. It was doubtless slow, halting, at times imperceptible, but always explorative, groping, varying, with many a set-back, many a dead-end. There were valleys of failure, obliteration and extinction, but also peaks of attainment, adaptation, success! Even those who feel that the pageant has no director admit that it achieves something of direction; that it has ascent and momentum; that it is cumulative, and notwithstanding wreckage and waste, has produced mankind with future possibilities outweighing his present limitations.

Man belongs to the phylum Chordata, which has as its distinction a flexible internal supporting rod along the back, jointed in all but the most simple forms. This rod, the notochord, extending from head to tail, is found in the embryo of every vertebrate. In most vertebrates the notochord is much reduced or missing in the adult, where it is replaced by the vertebral column, or back bone.

In his embryonic development man grows from a single fertilized cell to a multicellular organism, adding system after system such as animal groups had established in the remote past; repeating the steps, often with short-cuts or abbreviations, taken by his progenitors.

After many branchings due to diversifications, many explorative paths leading to extinction, the line most easily recognizable as ancestral for man is the group of fishes, the first chordates with a vertebral column. Man belongs to the great subphylum of *vertebrates,* a series of animals with a jointed backbone, including all the other warm-blooded, hairy creatures with which man is closely connected and also such different forms as birds, reptiles, amphibians and fishes. These all share the hollow tube formed by the vertebrae along the back side of the body and containing the main nerve trunk called the spinal cord. At the fore-end there is always some kind of skull, containing the brain, a complicated central switchboard for the nervous system with its connecting nerves and sense organs of the type which human beings possess.

There are two pairs of jointed appendages (fins in fishes) attached to the internal skeleton. The various paired appendages of vertebrates are structurally similar. It would be difficult to understand why the skeletal supports of these paired appendages of man, bats, whales, reptiles, amphibians, and even the traces of hind legs in snakes, should be structurally alike unless they had evolved from a common pattern, as variations of a basic plan. Their diversity of function suggests that an original, primitive skeletal pattern has been modified in becoming adapted to different uses—grasping, flying, swimming, walking, etc. In all these appendages corresponding (homologous) bones are found in similar relations to each other.

Fishes came into being while all life was still water-living. This earliest class of the subphyla (vertebrates) first showed the symmetry, the mobility, the characteristic activity, involving an internal skeleton with a powerful series of body-moving muscles attached to it. Entirely water-living, the tail was its chief means of locomotion. Breathing was by means of gills. Human embryos and those of all other vertebrates show typical paired gill-slits in early stages of their embryonic development. Although some of the skeletal supports of these are put to new uses, they serve as an illustration of the true though somewhat overworked principle of the recapitulation of the history of the race in the development of each new individual.

Man, in addition to his embryonic gill-slits, has kept, as a legacy from fishes, an internal skeleton of the vertebrate type with its plan of a hollow vertebral tube and forward skull, filled by the spinal chord and brain. Man still retains two pairs of jointed appendages, much modified but attached to the internal skeleton. Man has the typical vertebrate nervous system initiated by these remote forebears some 500 million years ago.

The class of amphibians bridges the gap between fishes and evolving land forms. Had no continents emerged from earth's all-engulfing oceans, life would have remained entirely water-living. The oldest strata of rock, having fossils of land plants, bear also fossils of amphibians. Molds of their footprints are found as are fossils of lung-fishes which were foreshadowed even while all life was water-living. Land-living was a very radical change, making new demands on the mechanics of respiration, of locomotion and of nerve stimulation. The jointed appendages were used for sprawling along the ground, but these gradually acquired fingers and toes and became able to raise the bodies of some types from the ground. Gills, either temporary or permanent, were present in all forms, but *lungs,* foreshadowed in the later fishes, developed as new equipment for land-living; scales disappeared. But the group as a whole was anchored to near-by waters by its method of reproduction. The eggs, laid and fertilized in the water, developed as had those of their gill-breathing, tail-propelling ancestors. The new individuals attained legs and lungs while still living in the water, emerging later for land-living in the manner familiar to us in present-day amphibians—our frogs, toads and salamanders. But because earth's pools grew less reliable as watery cradles for the young, this group has shrunken and grown less and less important. Legs and lungs, however, persist, an essential factor in man's making, a heritage from his ancient amphibian lineage some 400 million years ago.

Reptiles are vertebrates with horny scales and claws. They breathe by lungs and are largely land-living. There are innumerable fossil-forms as well as the present-day lizards, snakes, turtles, and tortoises, crocodiles and alligators. Their earliest fossils are found with the great tree-like horse-tails and club mosses, which matched in size and impressiveness the newly evolved animals. One fossil group is important as the probable progenitor of mammals; another, the dinosaurs, as the undoubted ancestors of birds.

During the long ages through which this class of vertebrates flourished and became dominant, a radical but successful innovation came into being through internal fertilization of eggs. A smaller number of eggs was fertilized within the body of the mother where each could then be stored with food (yolk), enclosed within a membrane containing fluid (white), making an individualized, unfailing pool. Before being laid, it was encased within a porous shell which allowed exchange of gases. This provided for a more advanced maturity of the young and some measure of added safety, compared with amphibian methods of reproduction. There was no caring for the young beyond placing the eggs in suitable surroundings. When hatched, the young were able to fend for themselves. A few kinds were born alive, the eggs hatching before they were laid.

Complete land-living for most orders and freedom of range was an achievement of reptiles. But they were hampered by their most successful special feature, their heavy armor of scales. Cold-bloodedness kept its restraining limitation upon them; there was no control of body temperature. Although reptile hearts had become partially divided, the pure and impure blood was mixed as in ancestral forms.

Few more imposing creatures enter the framework of evolution nor stay in it longer on earth and in air or in water. Handicapped by their strongest points, however, they gave way to descendants who developed new ways of living, greater activity when heavy scales were absent, and control of heightened temperatures for quickened body processes.

The large yolk sac, empty and useless, present in man's embryonic development, is considered a heritage from this large-yolked ancestry, which, with the internal fertilization of eggs, is the contribution reptiles established as their forward steps in evolution. Their dominance declined, however, before upheaval of climatic conditions could have caused it. It is thought that their downfall was hastened because other animals ate their unprotected eggs—an available source of highly lifted energy.

Birds are not included in the groups of animals through which man has descended. Their fossils show intermediate forms which have teeth like those of reptiles, long jointed tails bearing feathers, and wings with claws. Feathers have the same chemical composition as scales, and birds have scales on their feet. All the evidence convinces zoologists that birds appeared at about the same time as primitive mammals from reptilian stock. They share with mammals the characteristic of complete division of the heart and separation of pure and impure blood streams.

Mammals, the class of vertebrates to which man belongs, are characterized by hair and mammary glands. They first appeared in primitive forms while reptiles were still dominant more than 200 million years ago, establishing their most characteristic features and becoming dominant about 60 million years ago when conifers and cycads filled the forests. They include nearly all the larger animals now living on the earth, as well as whales, dolphins, and porpoises which live in the sea, and bats which may be said to inhabit the air. The circulatory system has complete division of the heart—the blood in transit from the lungs to the body on one side, and in transit from the body to the lungs on the other. This, coupled with a complicated and effective respiratory system, makes for the quickened chemical processes required by the greater degree of organization and activity in the mammalian group. The regulation of body temperature by sweat glands and insulating hair is a new factor in adjustment to varying demands in tempo and range of activity involving changes of climate. During the ages when mammals were rising to dominance, they showed great increase in proportional brain size, even among the most primitive sub-classes. This increase took place chiefly in the cerebral hemispheres, originally dedicated largely to the sense of smell.

It was their method of reproduction, however, which brought about their permanent success. Only the most primitive mammals, such as the duckbills, lay eggs. In most of the groups, the eggs are retained within the body of the mother until they hatch. In some (a sub-class Placentalia) a complicated mechanism called a placenta develops whereby the embryo is attached within the uterus and is nourished from the mother's bloodstream until birth. For a varying period of infancy after birth, the young are fed by milk from the mammary glands. Thus the prenatal food supply, no longer limited to the amount that can be stored within a shell, is available in a circulating stream, while wastes are removed by the same transportation system. The period of dependency of the infant upon milk from its mother, involving encouragement of psychic factors, varies in different orders of mammals.

One group which took a new path is the order of primates, a significant name. They are distinguished by a single pair of thoracic mammae (breasts), by five digits with flat nails on both hands or feet, and by opposable thumb or great toe. In an early period, primates took to tree-living, hands, feet and tails becoming prehensile. Under the new conditions the sense of smell became less important than the sense of sight; eyes slowly moved to the front, snouts shortened.

The conversion of the front pair of appendages into arms with hands was advanced much farther during this kind of living, but the step which freed them for still more varied uses came when these tree-dwellers again took to earth, attaining an upright posture. If you have seen a chimpanzee stand on his two legs and remain standing, you have had a faint but revealing preview of what took ages to attain—an upright posture. The posture itself involved difficulties and decided disadvantages anatomically, but it had the far-reaching and most significant result of freeing the hands.

The combination of curiosity and hands free for *handling* led to a more stimulating existence than ever before. Hands could fashion tools for special purposes, their owners having previously discovered that objects lying about could extend the effectiveness of hands. The use of tools and the fashioning of them for definite purposes was a radical step in controlling environment on a long path toward furthering mental development and evolutionary progress.

In addition to man, living primates include the lemurs of the old world tropics; tarsoids of the East Indies; the much larger group of anthropoids which comprises the New World or South American monkeys as well as the much more complicated Old World monkeys—the great man-like apes, the gibbon, the orangutan, the chimpanzee and the gorilla. In considering these, Professor Romer says, "We are climbing our own family tree." Man belongs to the sub-order Anthropoidea whose hands and feet are differentiated, and whose thumb or great toe is opposable. Finger and toenails are flat except in the marmosets, which have claws.

Three sections of anthropoids are recognized. These are (1) the South American monkeys with broad nasal septum, three premolar teeth in each half jaw (except the marmosets which, like the Old World monkeys, have two), and climbing feet; (2) the Old World monkeys and the great apes, with a narrow nasal septum, two pre-molar teeth, and climbing feet; (3) Bimana, also with narrow nasal septum, and two premolars, with the great toe non-opposable, and walking feet.

Man is classified as the genus *Homo,* and the species, *sapi-*

ens. Man is now believed *not* to have come directly from this group of anthropoids, but with them from various centers of primate stock. Bone for bone, muscle for muscle, organ for organ, the resemblances are convincing. The chief differences seem due to the methods of getting about and to the increase in proportional brain size which in man is two or three times that of the ape. Except for size and the much greater development of the regions associated with speech and the higher mental faculties, all the details of the human brain are like that of the smaller ape.

Most mammals are able to oxidize uric acid to soluble allantoin. Man is not able to do this, and therefore is liable to gout. Though most monkeys oxidize uric acid, man's inability is shared by the chimpanzee and the gorilla—in fact by all the tailless apes.

Chemical tests in blood analysis indicate that the blood of different kinds of animals is chemically similar in proportion to their structural resemblance. The use of blood transfusions has made blood types common knowledge. Human blood groups are found in apes but, with the exception of Rh groups, not in monkeys. It may be safer in some cases to have a transfusion from a chimpanzee than from your next of kin.

Man is distinguished from other primates by a nose with a bridge and a tip, by a median furrow in the upper lip, by out-rolled lips that show the lining membrane, and by his chin. Man has a lumbar curve in his spine, non-opposable great toes, arched feet, canine teeth not greatly larger than other teeth, a relatively large brain, comparatively bare body, and an unlimited habitat.

The oldest of fossil men most resemble apes. The more recent they are, the more they resemble modern man. The fact that none of these fossil types may have been the direct ancestor of Homo sapiens in no way lessens the significance of the evidence which proves that the brain of man reached its full size before the face became refined through the shrinking of the canine teeth and the beetling eyebrows. The last acquisition of the human face as we know it today was the chin.

The study of human ancestry has all come within the last century, beginning in the 1860's. The time lapse since man arose in the Pliocene Age was formerly estimated at 2 million years, but the application of radioactivity—that most accurate of time clocks for estimating the age of rocks—extends the time to 13 million years.

Much that has been discovered since 1935 is not yet incorporated into the general fund of what we know about fossil men. The yield of skulls and skeletons from the rich fields of south and east Africa is not yet available in any but special publications. Discoveries in China as well as Africa necessitate our reorientation. The paleontological evidence leads to an inescapable conclusion that the modern so-called races of man are not simultaneous divergents from a single stock, but do indicate much independent evolution, partly divergent, partly parallel from diverse ancestral stocks on the different continents.

Modern interpretations of the cumulative evidence indicate multiple centers of man's evolution involving certain interesting parallelisms. These go back ultimately, Gates tells us in *Human Ancestry* (1948), to parallel mutations occurring repeatedly as all mutations do, whether or not they have any survival value.

Estimates of the relation of the great apes to men have varied widely. These differences are based on very technical points in anatomy. Straus (1947) believes that four lines—monkeys, gibbons, great apes and man—evolved independently with many parallelisms, indicating the possessions of many of the same genes, occurring with varying frequencies. Gates feels that we need a tentative anthropological history of man from a genetical point of view. He believes that "Only by learning how man has come to his present state may we hope intelligently to control in any measure his future development." [14]

Is evolution something more than a sequence of successive changes? In the evolutionary process we must admit that with the many lines leading up, there are many leading down. Progression, adaptation, permanence have running contrasts in retrogression, maladjustment and extinction. But the curve made by tracing life's development from its first stirrings to man, whose mind can question and partly discover the process whereby he came to be, surges across the graph of evolutionary history with statistical certainty. Many points lie below the curve, but many more rise above its average sweep. Man alone can see the possible significance of this and interpret its implications. He sees himself as a part of nature, continuous with it, but distinguished from other natural creatures by a conscious self which can know that it is natural but also responsible, which can learn but also fail to grasp the significance of what he knows.

The upward sweep of the graph of evolution's long history, therefore, suggests that evolution itself may be the mechanism of a more basic process. The persistent, continuous, cumulative lifting of the levels of *organization* in living things is fundamental in nature.

But what of the originative factors in evolution and the rising powers of organization? Can either of these factors claim credit for such innovations as the chemical production of chlorophyll and its relation to food for all life on earth, the presence of haemoglobin with its hunger for oxygen as a constituent of blood, the internal skeleton, such physical triumphs as the penetration by lung sacs of the bones of birds, the equilibrative control of the chemical content of blood, the distribution of the knowingness of genes to every cell, the capabilities of the human brain?

There is good reason for thinking that nature's creative impulses are from a source more cosmic than any processes of evolution and its mechanisms, or of organization, or of life—something indicating an activity more like that of mind. Could it be mind?

CHAPTER FOUR

The Nature of Mind

Appreciation of the part mind plays in human experience suggests that an examination of its qualities may provide a clue to the nature of the directive factor whose presence, illusive but persistent, is indicated in some of the problems discussed.

Mind is so closely associated with a brain in popular thought, however, that we may be inclined to dismiss it as impossible in cell activities and in cosmic mechanisms such as heredity. In the same way electrons were associated with wires before certain assumptions were accepted as safe paths to truth if used in the experimental spirit and if tested by new techniques for reaching truth.

The presence of mind and the advent of consciousness are features of the evolutionary processes of our universe more puzzling to the scientist than that of life itself. Did the conscious arise from the unconscious, the self-knowing from the un-knowing, the sentient from the non-sentient? Can mental qualities evolve from non-mental sources? If so, how did any portion of matter-energy, either animate or inanimate, by evolution or any other process, ever become aware of itself, self-observing, self-measuring, self-directing—conscious? Is there a difference of nature between the "dust" from which man's body is made and his self-surveying mind? Are mind and body partners in the enterprise of living, giving evolution a double role to play in producing a two-fold nature in man? How could any two partners work together so perfectly as one? If there is but one, which one?

There are no answers of fact to these questions of ours but the asking may quicken our minds to the significance and difficulties of the problems of the existence of consciousness in a physico-chemical world—the world of science. Its presence, its association with living systems, its part in evolution, are basic problems in theoretical biology. Its meaning is the central problem of all philosophies. With its solution are bound up any beliefs we may hold about the nature of man and his destiny. The answer to these questions may hold significance for every human life because they extend or limit every human undertaking.

The heart of the puzzle in our search is the relation of the nature of consciousness and mind to a physico-chemical universe. Is our universe a minded reality with mind as well as matter-energy a part of the constitution of the stuff of the world? This might account for the knowingness of organization—the seeming foreknowledge of an agreed on plan to meet the needs of future functions in living systems. It is not the business of science to pass a verdict on the nature of the universe. Eddington says, "Scientific investigation does not lead to the knowledge of the intrinsic nature of things." We can formulate the basic question into three parts. Are mind and body two primary realities whose cooperation in living systems is too perfect to be true? Is mind a product of body? Is body a product of mind?

If this last question seems strange to you, consider what happens when you plan to go skating. That plan, which comes first, is a *mental* process, but you never think to take your body with you as you take your skates. What you plan, you do, not as partners but as a self whose plans are your plans—whose body is your body.

Any living body is characterized by a group of observable activities which keep the organism an identifiable individual from birth to death. If we are inclined to think of consciousness as one of these activities, we are reminded that consciousness is *unobservable* to anyone except the person experiencing it. It always has to be inferred by anyone else. Consciousness is characterized by the invisible quality of *feeling,* a sensitiveness to surroundings, an awareness of benefit or injury, pleasantness or unpleasantness, which we call pleasure or pain. We do not know if there are any organisms without it. We cannot judge if a tree is indifferent to being cut down. Dixon in his Gifford Lectures, *The Human Situation,* says: "Life is one, and, we may add, consciousness in some form is to be found where life is to be found, dreaming as in plants, half awake as in animals, or wide awake as in ourselves." [15]

A living organism acts *as if* it were interested in itself, its preservation, and its perpetuation. Consciousness adds the *fact* of interest to this appearance of interest. How this is possible no one fully understands, but this is undoubtedly the point where mental events enter as a factor in the evolution of organic life. For is there not all the difference in the world between an action and the consciousness of that action as being done by me? It is the difference, let us say, between a ball mechanically rolled down a bowling alley and a mythical ball intent on bowling itself, skillfully rolling itself toward the head pin and feeling satisfaction in the resulting ten strike.

This power of intent—initiative, self-survey, self-appraisal—is perhaps the most convincing experience in establishing the reality of human consciousness and mind. It is related to selfhood and distinguishes the history of a mind from the history of an adding machine or other response-mechanisms. Self is something more than a collection of single data (experiences and memories); it is a background on which these are collected, called "I," "myself."

As used here, the relation of the term consciousness to that of mind suggests the relation of weather to climate. *Consciousness* refers to the awareness and other mental processes of an individual at any given time. It is passing, temporary, clear or cloudy, as is weather. Mind may be cosmic, but each individual mind is inclusive, cumulative, a totality of mental processes throughout the lifetime of the individual, as climate is the total of the weather of any given region.

Some people believe that consciousness and mind are like weather and climate in being a result of responses to chance forces that play upon them and through them. But weather, as far as we know, never inquires into those forces and its reactions to them, rejecting some, accepting others; never has intentions, plans and purposes. Climate lacks the self-knowingness that examines its own nature and chooses a course of action. Because of these capacities is mind a thing apart in the world of nature?

There are still staunch mechanists, though their number is waning, who consider consciousness unimportant. They cannot believe that it can change events in a physico-chemical world. The one whom I know best, however, accepted anesthetics for recent surgery. Because all awareness, all values, and importances are wiped out when consciousness is lost, because without it there is no perception nor knowledge, no judgment nor enjoyment, others such as vitalists and idealists may consider it the most important single fact in the universe.

How the capacity for awareness is related to the ability to *do something about it,* no one tells us, but the connection is a reality, a deep-seated quality of living things, serving the *will to live.* It is an effective and essential factor in self-preservation, self-renewal, which no mere mechanism ever possesses. The process is seen most simply where the adjustment is made through movement. Some believe that all awareness is a functional matter wherein we try to use all observed relations.

In one of his early experiments, Jennings placed his protozoa (one-celled paramecium) in a trough where the water was kept hot at one end, cold at the other. He observed that the creatures would swim at random in many directions until they reached either the hot or cold water, when they would back, turn in a new direction, and proceed until they bumped into something or came again to the hot or cold water, when the backing and turning was repeated. Eventually, all would gather in the region between the extremes of temperature. This may be considered a process of individual adaptation through trial and error. Yet there are no nervous systems in these microscopic, unicellular animals. The elaborate structures and functions that serve the consciousness of higher animals are wholly lacking. The basis of awareness, its sensitivity to surroundings, followed by adaptive behavior, is part of the constitution of the organized protoplasm of each creature's one cell, which has its own simpler structures and functions. Apparently there is some differentiation in its sensitivity, some selection in its response. Is this the basis of mental processes? Is the use of trial and error an evidence that protozoa can keep an end in view, venturing a new procedure when an old one fails? Does their eventual avoidance of the ends of the trough prove that they can learn and profit by experience? No machine can do either. We usually attribute these qualities to mind. These two capacities are the initial qualities which consciousness has contributed to life, to the evolution of mental processes and through them to the evolution of mind. Lotze's mechanical beetle never falls off the table, but it cannot keep an end in view, nor can it learn by experience. Its mechanism strictly determines its action.

However humble and insignificant consciousness was when it entered the framework of evolution, it now seems to be evolution's most effective implement, its most promising field, its key activity. Through mental processes and resulting mind, consciousness may be considered the dominant feature in evolution. Mind seems to be the source of man's control over the changes he brings about in the plants and animals he raises for his use. Mind seems the basis of the increasing control man has over his environment through dams, power plants, tunnels, mines, roads, machines, transportation, communication, flood-control, irrigation, air conditioning, lighting, through warfare and all the arts and sciences of peace.

Whatever the functions of consciousness, it is undoubtedly the basis of what we call mind. With the increasingly complicated development of the nervous system, animals come to have sensations, perceptions, feelings and images. In addition to these processes, human beings form ideas about objects and their relations, make theories about their own natures and that of the world they live in. They have purposes and carry out plans. We use the word *mind* to include this whole range of conscious and intentional activities.

Modern psychologists tell us that they do not think of mind as a reality into which experiences may be fitted and stored, nor as something "unanalysable and mysterious." You may find now and then a textbook in psychology whose index does not list the word *mind.* As a typical definition we are told that "Mind is the name given to the sum of all the responses and accompanying introspectively known events of an individual; the total organization of experience and personality." [16] Does the term "sum" seem too passive to fit your experiences of mind as *wanting to know,* trying to find out, reaching out for new relations as well as constantly integrating experiences? It is difficult for some of us to be satisfied with trying to explain the infinite variety and complexity of mental life in terms of the "sum of all the responses"—the bodily activity of the nervous system—

complicated though it is. If the more active and discriminating processes are covered by the phrase "introspectively known events of an individual," the sum would still seem to have to do the summing, which no sum ever does. Just as a living organism is more than the additive sum of its parts, so mind, with its factors organized and integrated, seems to be more than a sum of responses and experiences. As life is impossible to interpret completely in terms of mechanism because you always start with something already living, so mind is difficult to keep within the category of mechanism because of this capacity to inquire into its own construction—the element of consciousness, as something given, something pre-existent, something deeper than matter.

Sometimes it seems as if everything in psychology that is accepted as an agreed-on fact turns out to be not about the mind but about the body.

This means that psychology in so far as it is scientific, that is to say in so far as it deals with fact, is physiology not psychology. The modern position expresses it—either there is no such thing as mind, or if there is, then everything which happens in the mind is a mere reflection of something which has first happened in the body.

Modern psychology aims to be scientific, to keep its thinking based on fact, to avoid speculation without observation to support it. We need its help in reconciling the introspective "me" (including its domain of mind and spirit) with the world of flesh and blood, of macro-molecules and hydrogen-ions with which the former seem so inexplicably connected. As the basis of all human experience, mind and consciousness must not be left out even if they are not describable in terms of observed facts.

Modern psychology has made many valuable contributions to understanding human nature. Its applications to the treatment of mental diseases, to the processes of learning, to the practices in education, in industry, in politics, in advertising, in warfare, indeed in every field where human beings can be *managed,* have all had some success. But many human beings object to being managed by others. They like to feel that they make their own decisions. They balk at being managed. They consider self-direction, self-control the only intrinsic sources of a claim to self-respect.

We have all had the experience of being moved to action by propaganda. If I realize that another's belief is being used to influence me, I question the motive of the propagandist —my mind is likely to oppose his. Herein lies one difference between the working of mind and that of a machine whose matter never discriminates between motives in their stimuli. It is difficult to follow the working of cause and effect in minds when the reasons for decisions are intangibles which have no physical counterparts, no substantial existence in space to serve as stimuli. Duty, loyalty, honor, justice, patriotism, conscience, scruple, as well as avarice, hypocrisy and many unattractive qualities are all values held by minds. Each means more to some minds than to others. Each motivates action with a power measurable only by its worth to the individual, and as this valuation is unpredictable, so also are the reactions to it.

The nature of mind responds to value-thinking as well as

to causal-thinking. This is because man is more than a biological machine, more than a thing to be used and worked. A thing has value only so long as you need or use it. A thing is not an end in itself; but a person, because of his mind with its values, has a different status. His worth is objective, independent because it is based on what a person is—a free being, capable of an ethical point of view and of responsibility in a society of rational beings. Our failure to recognize this principle may be the basis of our inability to understand the nature of mind and its place in mankind and in the universe. Man must be respected as an end because he is free, not caused. Kant's categorical imperative is as true today as when he wrote it (1785), a command without an *if*. "So act as to treat humanity, whether in thine own person or in any other, in every case as an end withal, never as a means only."

To some thinkers, the distinction between mind and body seems a false abstraction since they are separable in thought only, not in experience. If you are inclined to take mind at face value, with no far-reaching implications, you may accept Julian Huxley's description of mind as "an always present mental aspect of material forms in all their activities," [17] and let it go at that, but the relations of mind to space-time and matter-energy are a challenge to further thinking. The general acceptance of relativity and quantum theory make it imperative that these relations should not be ignored. Descartes said long ago that *thinking,* the essence of mind, is not an event in space. No mental processes today are considered events in space. Mind has no spatial relations, as have all products of the body. We speak, figuratively only, of a man as broad- or narrow-minded. However dependent mental processes may be on neural currents or on other physiological processes in space, they are rarely regarded as identical with them or with the stimuli which cause them.

The body has relations of distance to objects outside itself. Its parts are above or below, in front of or behind, far or near each other. But that is not true of mind nor of any mental events. To a given body there is only one space; to a given mind there are many possible spaces.

But both physical and mental events are in time—before or after or at the same time. Every event, whether of body or mind, must take time. There is no such thing as an instantaneous event. But let us consider if there are differences in the time spans of mental and of physical events. The physical event seems to be all in the present. Its duration is observable, measurable, bringing changes which require time to come to pass. But such an event is not cumulative. Such traces as it leaves are present facts. They cannot be regarded as memories because there is no true retention of a past in matter. There are traces of its past in an old shoe, or a rock, or a brain, but in a mind there is real retention.

This gives mind a special relation to time. The physiological processes in nerves and brain, accompanying mental activity, are in the present only; but because of the changes that past activities have caused in the nervous system, their patterns can be recalled, *reactivated.* Mind can summon past images and relations, hold them in focus to compare with the present. It can anticipate events which have not yet come to pass, a capacity which has been found to arise in childhood before imagination, as if image experiences originally arose in order to reach into the future instead of to bring back the past. These patterns are of varying degrees of permanence, but they are cumulative. Their duration piles up and can be summoned for use. Mind's whole past, theoretically, can be brought into the field of its present-time vision.

Mind's relation to matter-energy is also puzzling. There are no quanta of mind, though a quantum of the brain's functioning may some day be found. No physicist as yet admits mind as a form of energy, however dynamic it may seem. Mind has no resemblance to any quality or property of matter such as color, hardness, weight, or warmth, which are passive. Mind is not an element in the world of Ultra-physics. Mind does not enter into the calculations of the scientist except as that which does the calculating. You can not think that mind is a passive quality of matter when its most striking characteristics are its spontaneity, its meaningful and synthetic activity, its cumulative quality, its purposefulness, its end-seeking persistence, its discernment of values, its creative capacity, its increasing dominance in evolution.

It has become an integral part of the theory of relativity that the mind of the observer must be taken into account before we can know how much space or time or motion we are dealing with. Whether the observer is represented by a clock, a meter stick, or the revolving drum of a recording instrument, the observer's mind is behind its choice and perhaps behind its invention and construction as well, and thus is brought into the reckoning. It is the scientist's mind alone which can use and interpret the record. This has brought a sense of defeat to those conservatives who thought that mechanism would some day reign supreme.

Psychologists, as well as all other scientists, must of necessity be thorough-going mechanists in their method of work, but as men they need not hesitate to say with Sir Thomas Browne: "There is something in us that can be without us and will be after us though indeed it hath no history what it was before us and cannot tell how it entered into us." To help you reach your belief about the nature of mind, consider the ancient intuition that the nature of things is better seen in what they come *to* than in what they come *from.*

The expectation of Herbert Spencer's time, that mind would eventually be explained by extension of chemical laws, has not been realized. The fact that mind can be conditioned by such chemicals as drugs and anesthetics does not prove that it is wholly chemical in its nature. Accompanied by chemical processes it certainly is, as is any living activity, and conditioned by chemistry; but all phenomena in nature are conditioned in some way. Consciousness is no exception.

To many there seems to be evidence that mind can condition bodily chemistry in turn. The studies of Cannon and his co-workers on ductless glands show that emotions have direct effect on their activities. With the flow of adrenalin there follow other physiological effects—quickened blood flow, faster breathing, increased liberation of blood sugar and added production of red blood cells—a physical basis for the heightened powers which come to an individual under such emotional excitements as emergencies, calamities, battles, even extremes of good fortune.

The status of the basis of emotions, however, is still open

to experiment. If you have experienced the lifting of group morale and mass emotion by oratory, and felt it bracing all the forces and increasing all the energies of human beings, did you find initiation of the critical changes seeming to lie with the mind or with the body? Such stability of reserve power as is indicated by Gandhi's fasts, and by survivors who drifted 83 days on a raft, also has yet to be explained on a physical basis. It appears to be due to a supreme mastery of the human spirit over the demands of the body.

If this is possible, then you intrude intangible and incalculable mental factors into the otherwise regular and calculable processes of nature. No one can point out the time nor the spot where the interaction takes place. On this crucial point there are no observed facts.

There seems to have been no question in regard to this matter in the minds of the compilers of the *Coast Guard Wartime Safety Measures*. It states on page 120, "Experience has shown time and time again that the comfort and indeed the chances of survival of those adrift depend upon the frame of mind of the boat's company." There are no qualifying clauses, no "other things being equal." There are many survivors who believe that the statement is true. As to how many times it may have failed to be true, we have no witnesses.

Scientific psychologists sometimes believe that mind can condition bodily processes, but they do not call this mind. They explain that because the autonomic and cerebrospinal nervous systems work together, the neural basis of our feelings may change the neural basis of our thoughts and ideas very decidedly; and thus our ideas appear to influence our bodily processes and to produce very intense feelings. The status of this problem is still a field for experimentation.

Experimental work on the effect of the glands of internal secretion—the ductless glands (adrenal, thyroid and others)—and on the content of the blood aroused great interest in changes worked on intelligence and personality. But the extravagant hopes that whole racial levels of mentality might be lifted by use of drugs have not been realized. No drug is yet known which will lift a level of intelligence and keep it lifted.

At present you may not be able to decide the questions: *Is mind a product of the body and its nervous system?* Or *is mind a primary reality implementing itself through the nervous system as its special mechanism?* Whether the mind *is* a mechanism or *has* a mechanism is a controversial question. Able investigators have pictured for us the stages whereby the nervous system has evolved throughout the animal series from simplest obscurity in lower animals to significant dominance in human beings.

Those scientists who are genetic psychologists have gathered a vast collection of data concerning the genesis and development of *psychological processes* throughout the animal series from the simplest to the most complex and also data concerning the development of many kinds of individuals from their single-celled beginnings through old age to death. There is still need for gathering up all that is known about the nervous system and all that we have found out about mental life and its psychological processes into a unified, synoptic view.

Since the middle of the nineteenth century, the human

mind has been usually regarded by biologists as a function of the brain, with its definite regions connected with each process—speech, vision, motion, etc. This regional location is undeniable—though if one center is destroyed, other centers sometimes take over the lost function. If, however, we regard mind as a function of the brain, we must admit the defectiveness of all those methods of explanation for which physiological processes account for only physiological results. The processes of the brain as an organ within an organism, part of the machinery of physical nature, can explain many observed matters of reflex action, instinct, habit, and other factors in behavior. But when we inquire into the creative qualities of human mind which have resulted in our great bodies of knowledge—music, mathematics, philosophy, and all the arts, astronomy and all the sciences—difficulties are disclosed in regarding self-conscious mind as an object in nature subject wholly to laws of cause and effect. Can this view tell the whole truth about mind? Undoubtedly, mind has a wonderful mechanism, the nervous system. Is it something more than this mechanism?

In protozoa we found the mechanism which gives the capacity for awareness of surroundings and adaptive response possessed by the protoplasm of the creature's single cell. All living protoplasm has a kind of sensitivity we call excitability. In all animals, the protoplasm of each cell is excitable, but in multicellular animals certain kinds of cells are specialized to carry on this particular function for the whole organism. Specialization and division of labor among cells is characteristic of all complicated animals. Nerve cells, called neurons, are particularly excitable and carry on the work of awareness and adaptation; muscle cells and glands bring about appropriate behavior. It is an amazing mechanism, this receptor-neuro-effector system, with its details of structure and function. To many it seems a perfect response mechanism.

Scientists have devised robot chess players which are rarely in error. As for the automatic telephone system, could anything more perfect be designed as a substitute for human intelligence? While the success of these various inventions does not prove that their mechanisms are the same as a living brain, it certainly suggests it. To many of us it makes the hypothesis of physico-chemical causes derived by physiologists from their data both more interesting and more challenging.

Comparative anatomists know many details of the structure of the nervous system, both in its larger features and in its microscopically visible cells. Embryologists know each stage of its development: how neurons form and grow and establish their connections with sense organs and muscles and glands and with each other; that neurons in human beings are practically all formed before birth; that among the estimated 12 billion neurons in the human brain alone, some 9 billion, 200 million are in the cerebral cortex. Genetic psychologists tell us that the cortex is little used until higher centers are involved. They are sure that the methods by which uses are established and connections are made determine many factors in learning and in habit.

Biochemists know many facts of the intricate chemical composition of the nervous system, its metabolism, its production of heat and carbon dioxide when neural currents called impulses travel over it. These impulses are started when a stimulus activates a sense organ by physical means as in sight, hearing, temperatures, or pressures; or by chemical means as in taste or smell; or when an impulse goes from a center to muscles or glands.

Experts in the physics of light and sound pronounce the eye and the ear perfect instruments for their purposes; they can explain how each is made and how it works, but the seeing and the hearing by the conscious self they cannot explain.

Biophysicists have collected a growing mass of data about the electric phenomena of the nervous system: how the part of the neuron that is excited becomes electrically negative compared with the unexcited parts so that the impulse travels along as a lighted fuse of gunpowder would travel, if it were not for the neuron's *power of self-renewal* under normal conditions. They have devised wonderfully sensitive electronic instruments which measure and record the speed, intensity, duration and localization of neural currents.

Perhaps the most significant of these instruments is the device called the brain-writer, encephalograph, which records voltage changes in the electrical phenomena of the brain. Study of these records shows that the brain, besides serving as a switchboard where adjustments are made, is itself a center of activities, except in *deep sleep.* These activities can be studied by recording the electrical phenomena which accompany them. The recorded waves show that there are typical patterns of activity during sleep, mental work, emotional excitement, hypnotic control, and other experiences. Records made during health, sickness and insanity have distinctive characteristics. Under certain circumstances the physician is aided in his diagnosis of mental illness by a study of the patient's brain-wave record. It is interesting to note that there are family resemblances in the records of twins and of other relatives. Whether or not thinking is implemented by these phenomena, no one yet knows.

Physiologists claim as their field all the functions of the nervous system but not what Sherrington calls the "mysteries of mind." There are strange gaps in our knowledge of mental processes, notwithstanding all the scientific facts that have been assembled. No one knows how a pattern of nervous impulses can cause a sensation of pain in my consciousness nor how the stimulus of black marks on the yellow paper of a telegram can result in a complete change in the content of my mind. Whether the emotion is joy or sorrow, it seems strangely unrelated to any physical, chemical, or electrical change in any part of my nervous system.

Modern psychologists usually agree that mental processes are wholly and fundamentally dependent upon present and past sensory stimulation. The stimuli, however varied, are wholly chemical and physical; the response is physiological activity in the receptor-neuro-effector system with an indeterminate contribution from the introspectively known events of mental life. Some one has said, whether we regard the relations of matter to mind as inexplicable or as needing no explanation, science can discuss the relation between nervous impulses and sensations without attempting to decide how or whether the one can be caused by the other.

Comparative study of nervous systems has emphasized the fact that man differs from the other animals but slightly in general structure of sense organs and nerve fibers, while the difference in the size, complexity and capabilities of the brain is enormous. The usefulness of the brain in bringing about adaptive behavior (including language), in the interaction between man's organism and his surroundings, is obvious. In the nervous centers one function of ideas—or what stands for ideas—is to guide behavior. A true idea leads to a favorable response; a false idea to misjudgment and maybe to mishap. But the range and achievements of mental processes in human beings have gone far beyond the requirements for biological survival in the field of natural selection.

The proponents of mind as a primary reality, impressed by the accomplishment of human mind, ask: "Could all the varied structures and functions of the evolving nervous systems have become organs of mind if mind were not already present in the universe?"

Lloyd Morgan assumed that in the universe at large there is some *mental cause* for the emergence of mind in connection with the animal organism. This would necessitate the assumption of mind as a primary reality in the universe as being the source of all forms of mind. The inner urge of active human minds to know and to understand matters which have no practical import may be evidence of a cosmic reality, mind, behind the urge.

Biology as a science cannot answer that question, nor can any other science. But biologists recognize the limitations of their method as well as its wonderful possibilities. They are coming to know that in dealing with ultimate problems, biology as a mental product needs the help of all other lines of mental products—mathematics, science, logic, philosophy, religion, aesthetics, etc.

The place of mind in the universe is an ultimate problem. Mind may be a primary reality in the universe, developing through the mechanism of life and the nervous systems of living organisms.

Biology assures us that awareness and more awareness is the contribution made by life to evolving nervous systems. But *thinking,* the essence of mind, contributes new kinds of awareness, supplementing the reports of sense organs by discerning relations such as good habits to good health, by grasping meanings, integrating experiences, establishing values. These intangible factors are not directly contributed by sense organs, but they are acknowledged to act as controls of adaptive behavior through motivation. These invisible, imponderable features affect the response mechanism of the human nervous system. The human brain, as part of the mechanism for awareness and control, is a visible symbol of this most fundamental of human characteristics, control of behavior by consciousness and mind.

Whether we consider mind a primary quality of the universe or only a product of life, we can admit that many mechanisms have contributed to its growth and evolution. The shuffling of gene packs in biparental reproduction is such a mechanism, giving a wider range of individual differences. The wider the range, the greater the chance of favorable variations. The evolving nervous system is another such mechanism. Indeed, evolution itself may be considered as such a mechanism on a cosmic scale. However successful evolution may be as a process of establishing improvements and neglecting disadvantages through natural selection, does it possess creative powers, originative impulses? In your experience, what is the source of such impulses in yourself, your home, your community, your institutions, your government? Mind is the most creative reality in human experience. Perhaps creativity has some other source.

The fact that conscious mind is expressed, made manifest to us, through the medium of life is no proof that in its nature mind is a product or a property of life, ending when life ends, enduring only as life endures, not continuously in any one self, but through successive selves. Mind, the most synthesizing, purposive, evolving, cumulative, value-finding, creative factor we know in human existence, may be the most indestructible stuff in the universe—as real as atoms (even when smashable) with as truly hidden inner sources of power.

C. G. Jung, honored at the Harvard Tercentenary as the world's greatest living psychiatrist, thinks that it is an almost ridiculous prejudice to assume that existence can be only physical. Traditionally in modern science, such prejudice has been in favor of matter, spatial relations and mechanical causation, but relativity, quantum theory and nuclear physics have changed our concepts. We know that there are realities beyond reach of our senses.

Science is closer than ever before to accepting mind as a primary entity—to accepting its reality at the center of the universe rather than regarding it as a sprig from life's tree. Heralded by *relativity* and by *quantum theory,* metaphysical assumptions are being recognized in many phases of science. Led by the development of the super-sensible phases of physics, we have become more keenly aware of the momentous discovery that scientific realities are all concepts of the mind. Science admits that to the *external world,* the field of all its investigations, there is only one entrance—the *door* of *human mind.*

Long ago, a great thinker, Berkeley (1685-1753) said, "The sum of all reality consists of perceivers and perceptions, thinkers and their thoughts." He believed that the fragmentary world of direct perception is made by scientific thought into a complete and continuous whole; that the laws which science traces are realities because God's mind is behind them—a guarantee and the only guarantee of the interrelatedness and order of nature which is revealed by science.

Is mind the directive organizing factor in the universe, at the center of nature and its life? There is an ancient intuition that life is deeper than matter and mind deeper than life. Can you believe that in the beginning was mind?

CHAPTER FIVE

The Relation Between Mind and Body

In 1940 at the Memorial Service honoring Herbert V. Neal as zoologist and teacher, his friend, William Ernest Hocking, speaking of him as a "colleague in the teaching of philosophy," said in part:

> Evolution has produced marvelous organisms; but it has produced also something more marvelous—organisms which *are aware of* marvelous organisms, and which can consider the whole complex history debouching in themselves, and speculate about it. That nature has produced the human body is a marvel; that it has produced the Thinker is more marvelous still. . . . Could nature have evolved the human body without evolving the human mind? Answer yes or no. If we say yes, then the human mind remains on our hands as an unexplained fact in the world, and a useless fact, since it can have no influence on physical behavior; and our science remains incomplete at a radically important point, unless we take the desperate

alternative of pronouncing consciousness—including its products, art, literature, culture, science—as unimportant. If we say no, the mind *must have evolved* with the body, then we admit the defectiveness of all those methods of explanation for which physiological causes account for only physiological effects, and the mind remains outside the laboratory picture.

It is the uniqueness of the mind, and of life in general, which constitutes what we may call *the biologist's dilemma.* Granted that life is unique, shall it be attributed to a special power or faculty, a vital principle? Then we have to deal with an occult factor, and our experimental determinism is disturbed.

If there is no such special power, then life is a function of physico-chemical processes, at a special stage of complication—then life and mind should be open to synthesis under proper laboratory conditions. Even Jacques Loeb found the difficulties of such a program staggering.

Many biochemists believe that life in a simple form will some day be produced in a laboratory. But no one of them has expressed the faintest hope of being able to synthesize life that would *be* or *become conscious.* The inconceivably long time nature may have required for the process is not the only lacking factor. The intangible qualities of consciousness and mind are still more troublesome and unavailable features. They cannot be handled and added to any concoctions. They are inaccessible to sense. They evade all scales and test tubes, microscopes and meter-sticks as products of the body never do. Science no longer questions the existence of realities beyond the scope of its method or beyond the range of our sense perceptions. The development of electronics has proved that electrons and protons are just as real as if we could see them. If mind is conceded to be the source of human creativity, we must admit that the living body is the observable source of its activity, its chief implement, its present medium of manifestation. But these uses of the body either separately or together do not constitute a *source* of mind. We must look elsewhere for its *origin.*

When we, as present-day thinkers, long for a pillar of fire to lead us to the one true belief, we must remember that our unquestioning allegiance to that truth would rob us of the stimulus to thinking and investigation. In speculative matters we need a synthesis of all the facts, all the reasons, contributed by other lines of intellectual interpretation. In science, as in religion, faith has a very real function.

Mind and body, the psychical and the physical, are distinguishable in thought if not in experience. In our *thought,* mind and body have different relations to space-time and matter-energy. At present, mind remains inaccessible to sense while body may be observed, measured and tested by the various procedures of science. In our *experience,* mind and body seem to be one, an integrated unit however psychophysical, whose solidarity is inseparably one, asleep or awake. If in experience we cannot separate action and thought, part physical, part mental, do we need to do so in our thinking? They are both parts of an integrated individual whose history is *one* history; both work toward the same ends. Whatever you do, you do as a body-mind whole—a partnership, if you wish—but as a unit, a self. Sherrington in his Gifford Lectures says:

> Knowledge looking at its world had painfully and not without some disillusions arrived at two concepts; the one, that of energy which was adequate to deal with all which was known to knowledge, except mind. But between energy and mind science found no "how" of give and take. There was co-existence; that was all. To man's understanding the world remained obstinately double. Busy common sense went forward treating the twofold together as one.[18]

If this unity and integration are true, how do you account for the recurrence of the problem of the relation of mind and body in human thought and what Sherrington in the *New York Times* Magazine (May, 1950) calls the "hush-hush attitude" of present-day scientists toward it? Is the relation of mind and body a pseudo-problem based on a false division of experience, or is it one of the ultimate problems of our universe?

Touching life as it does at countless points, is the relation of mind and body too subtle to be captured for examination and settled? Sherrington, in his Rede Lecture (1933) says, "Yet nerve and brain are but a skillfully laid train of powder between the muscles it fires and the restless world which fires it. The question who turns the key, to use that simile, is soon answered; the outside world." [19] But is it an illusion that we control our behavior—our deliberate responses to this outside world—through the influence of the mental concepts which we call purposes, plans, intentions, standards, character, hopes, ambitions and aspirations? Who turns *these* keys? The outside world has no intangibles.

The human body is a physical object, an energy system among other physical objects; but it is apart from all other energy systems in having a double role to play. It is a part of physical nature and it is an instrument of a conscious-self. It is so closely integrated and incorporated with the self that uses it that they are often considered identical.

Because of the twofold role it has to play, the body appears to us to have two aspects: first, it is an organism, an energy-system of causes and effects, an object of all the biological sciences; and second, it is a "city of meanings whose every line and every motion is read for what it signifies." To some of us, the important character is the first, the reality of the body; for others, the second character is more important and *real* and the first is derived from it.

As a part of nature, the body has all the causal relations which science can discover in any energy-system and, in addition, whatever meanings belong to nature. Nature is an assemblage of common objects by means of which minds communicate; the body is accordingly a common object. Bodies, then, form part of the bridge between minds whose whole span is nature. Through them we are visible, audible, accessible to other minds. By means of them we can help and benefit or hinder and injure other selves.

The body, however, could not serve as the peculiar instrument of communication unless it were more directly controllable than the rest of nature. Energy is the usual vehicle of communication between minds. Thoughts are not energy, but speech is; emotions are not energy, but facial and bodily expression are. A philosophy of life is not energy, but behavior is. Few doubt the mental factors in these forms of expression, though their medium is energy. However far language and its social context go to make the man, there seems to be direct control of language by mind. Through speech, mind uses energy to convey its thought to another mind. Mind, then, may have some leverage it brings to bear upon the energy-system, the body. Let us examine this relationship.

Though other objects in nature may defy me, my body cannot help obeying me. It becomes, thus, a structure built by my disposition and reactions, both instinctive and deliberate. So we come to accept the body of any person as the most available symbol of the character of that person as well as the instrument of his will, expressed in his behavior.

Each body has a complicated system of intercommunicating associations and connections like an incredibly and infinitely complex automatic telephone switchboard. If modern physiological psychologists are inclined to consider this system wholly physical, they also claim that mental phenomena must be described in their own terms and that (to quote a letter from Dr. Leonard Carmichael) "an operational or positivistic approach to the identification of conscious terms such as the experience called 'green' in the phrase 'I see green' will often involve a description of the physical energies and the physiological states which are present at the same time or immediately before the reported conscious experience. This togetherness in time does not identify the physical or physiological with the experiential. It also surely does not guarantee that the often misused word 'cause' may be employed in stating observed or even quantitatively demonstrated relationships between recorded stimuli, known activity of the organism, and specific conscious experiences."

If sensation and impulse were the only factors involved in human action, the view which considers that what we call mind is merely a succession of more or less distinct but possibly unrelated responses would be ample. Its very simplicity would recommend its acceptance. But to some of us, the most significant aspects of the mind-body relationship in experience are not its automatic responses to stimuli, but the fact that with each biological, physical response there is also the reaction of the self as *knower*. I must recognize this sensation as a signal of a thing which summons me to investigate it and to put it in relation to other experiences. It is the response of the self as knower which is important to me rather than the automatic features of the mechanism of knowing.

While much human action is the result of mere impulse, mind seems to have a direct effect in guiding and determining the *purposeful* conduct, which expresses long-cherished standards and the character of the self. This human self seems more than a thing in nature because it is more than a fact: facts are not conscious of facts, but the self is. While facts are as they must be, the self feels free. Out of various possibilities the self feels that he chooses what shall be the next fact of action.

Mechanistic psychology says that the choice is a necessary consequence of the character which his nature and reactions to environment have given him—that a shrewd scientist could have predicted the decision. But others think that a *capacity for self-building* is an integral characteristic of a self, and the concrete expression of its freedom.

The mind is conscious of its own succession of experiences.

It seems to stand sufficiently apart from its experiences to feel its own continuity in contrast to the transition of events. But the self never feels automatic in its reactions except in such cases as when a smarting blow causes anger, a loud noise causes fright, or a parched throat causes thirst. In such cases, the natural mechanical reaction is no more free than that of a released spring. Freedom, in fact, consists of the power of the *self* to become aware of the network of physical causes in which its body is enmeshed, and in being aware of it, the self *becomes more real* than the *causal* setup. When I become aware that I am getting angry, then I am no longer absorbed in the reaction of anger, and the causes can continue to act in such direction as shall carry out my deliberate will. This power of self-survey, serving to re-direct my action to carry out my chosen purpose, is the factor which distinguishes the history of a mind from the history of any merely mechanical process. Mind knows its superiority to whatever is merely natural in itself, as Kant thought, because it deposes nature from master to servant of the free self. If these statements are true of your experience, you can give personal testimony on the leverage between mind and body. This should not be disregarded in deciding your position on this age-old problem.

We may gain an added perspective if we make a brief survey of the various solutions that have found adherents during the long history of human thought on the relation of mind and body. Whatever your own belief, you may find it stated among the following, chosen from many sources—first ancient, then modern. The persistence with which the problem has been studied has equalled its recurrence in the development of thought. In these statements of belief through the ages, the terms mind, soul, consciousness, thought, reason, will, are all used as broadly equivalent. Much might be said about distinctions, but not in connection with these statements made by others. Body, brain, organism and matter are also used as terms representing the physical reality. Wherever the term *matter* is used, its context will indicate whether the reality meant is that in use before or after the revolution in physics.

The crucial significance of the mind-body relationship as a problem is no new discovery. It is thought that primitive men all over the earth pondered it and were puzzled by it long before the Greek philosophers dwelt upon it.

The Greeks were the earliest thinkers to emphasize mind as unique in the world. To their keen intellectual interests, they brought great clarity of thought which became less dominated by religious or ethical motives than in earlier peoples. Matter-energy had loomed so large in the realities presented by life, that mind (so intangible and invisible) had been far less impressive. Its reality had to be asserted and defended.

Heracleitus (500-475 B.C.) taught that universal reason (mind), like a gentle enveloping flame, pervaded all activity in the world. Anaxagoras (500-428 B.C.) believed that mind, cosmic in proportions, embodying order, caused the evolution of the world from chaos, bringing life, organisms, and also mind and reasoning beings into existence. Plato (427-347 B.C.) saw the world as a system of ideas embodied in particular forms. To him the immaterial ideas were real and eternal while the material substance of its forms was defective and transitory. He believed the mind (soul) was enmeshed as in a prison and likely to reach a truer vision of reality after being freed from the body by death. Aristotle, the great pupil of Plato, found mind and body so inseparably joined in human beings that he believed the soul not something else than the body, but its very form, its inner life, fitting it as the hand the glove. He believed that mind is a function of the body. "If the eye were an animal, vision would be its mind." Purpose to him was the *final cause;* God the first cause.

The beginning of a new era came with Descartes (1596-1650), who thought that he must separate the self of which he felt so unquestioningly sure—"I *think,* therefore I *am"*—from the physical world: "res cogitans" from "res extensa." This establishment of a scientific difference between mind and body has long troubled the world. Modern psychology is not concerned with the mind and body relationship which is a metaphysical problem; but it has not dispelled the mystery that for hundreds of years has been felt in the relation between mind and body. To Descartes, man was an automaton with superadded mind; man's kindred, the brute creatures, were automata. He asserted the presence of mindless motor acts in both man and animals. He assumed that the motor act required an inhibitory process along with an excitatory one, which fact was confirmed 250 years later by experimentation. Descartes' reflexology of man as a mechanism, a robot actuating itself, is practically the position taken by Pavlov, the late Russian physiologist, Descartes' greatest successor, but an experimentalist, as Descartes never was.

Later, Spinoza (1632-1677) offered his solution of the

mind-body problem as the double-aspect hypothesis. To him, both mind and body were phenomena, two ways of looking at an underlying reality. Mental processes or *psychoses* parallel nervous processes or *neuroses*. But the reality of which they are manifestations escapes us. This underlying reality which mediates all relations, he thought, is one being, God, perfect, self-caused and the ground of everything that appears to us in experience, "absorbing both mind and matter into a single substance whose ultimate being is not so much neutral as unknowable."

George Berkeley (1685-1753) thought that our problems are made by ourselves. "We have first raised a dust, and then complain we cannot see." Qualities like shape and color are "ideas"; if they inhere in anything, they inhere in the mind which perceives them. He thought them produced in us by the only active thing we know, namely, a living spirit outside ourselves, surely not by an inert, material substance, but by another mind which acts directly upon us, *the mind of God*—world-mind.

Berkeley began his argument by an examination of the sense of sight, which was a useful beginning since nearly everyone thinks of the real world as the world his eyes reveal to him. He led his readers to view the world with him as a world within the mind, a world in which apart from consciousness there is nothing, hence no merely physical nature whatever.

He believed that the human mind is always forgetting its own part in making its experience. It fails to recognize color and sound as its own work and space as its idea. It forgets that "substance" is its own idea, by which it tries to bestow an independent existence upon its experience. He tried to establish the difference between reality and illusion. Nature is either all external to the observer, or else all within the observer's perception. He takes the latter alternative. For Berkeley, the sum of all reality is perceivers and their perceptions, thinkers and their thoughts.

This does not leave the great task of science without basis. Berkeley thought that the fragmentary world of direct perception is made by *scientific thought* into a complete and continuous whole, not by using substance but by using law—the undeviating way in which experiences succeed each other, depend on each other, and supplement each other to round out a whole-world picture.

Science has only recently made the momentous discovery that the only door to knowledge of any sort is the door of human mind. Berkeley tried to teach this two and a half centuries ago.

Kant (1724-1804), still more sensitive to the reality of mental processes as conscious phenomena, regarded Descartes' field of extension as a property or function of the mind itself; but he also believed that there was an unknowable reality outside the mind, at whose incentive the materials of sensation appear to us.

Kant believed that the mind is a factor in forming the world, which it seems to observe as an independent and self-operative object. In beholding and thinking the world, the mind builds also awareness of itself.

If you incline to the belief of the French physician, Cabanis (1757-1808), that thought is a function of the brain which secretes it as the liver does bile, science protests. A function is either a movement (a form of energy) or a secretion (a substance), both of which can be measured quantitatively. A secretion is as material as the organ which secretes it, and it can be collected in a test-tube and chemically analyzed; it may be weighed, and it occupies space just as any material does. The relation of thought to the brain is not like that of a secretion to an organ. An active brain does produce substances which pass from it by way of the blood, but among these products, as far as we know, there are no ideas or emotions. The modern materialist, now called naturalist, thinks of mind or consciousness either as a form of energy like heat or light produced by a brain, or, possibly and inconsistently, as a function in the mathematical sense of the word.

Some thinkers take the position of Buchner (*Force and Matter,* 1855) that the brain and its operations produce the mind. "The brain is the organ of thought and . . . these two, brain and thought, stand in such immediate and necessary connection that neither can exist without the other." But others protest that elsewhere in nature motion produces only motion. How can it be that in the brain, motion produces sensations and thought? It is important in our thinking to be quite clear on this point, for in common usage mind and brain are often used equivalently.

When in 1902, Minot maintained that consciousness was a device to regulate the actions of organisms so as to accomplish ends which are useful to the organisms and he argued that consciousness must stand in direct causal relations to physiological processes, he seemed a heretic to the mechanists, who could not believe that mind and consciousness could have any causal effect in a physical world. This lag in belief was general among biologists of that time. But Minot had strong sympathizers. They asked, "Why has consciousness evolved, as it certainly has evolved, if it is useless?" They were unable to conceive that the evolution of animals has taken place as they believe it has, unless consciousness is a real and dominant factor. Without it, Minot believed, "the universe might come to absolute rest." This conception of mind places it as a *primary* reality in the world. We shall later consider more fully beliefs about primacy in reality.

Modern physics is in strong opposition to such determinism. Eddington, who believes that mind has a function in world-building and self-building, says in connection with causation in *The Nature of the Physical World,* "Like most people, I suppose, I think it incredible that the wider scheme of nature which includes life and consciousness can be completely predetermined. . . . It is a consequence of the advent of the quantum theory that physics is no longer pledged to a scheme of deterministic law. Determinism has dropped out in the latest formulations of theoretical physics and it is at least an open question whether it will ever be brought back."[20] Heisenberg's Nobel Prize work on the quantum theory, known as the *Principle of Indeterminacy* sometimes called uncertainty, seems to have added another "knock-out blow" to mechanism as applied to the problems of life and mind.

Henri Bergson (1859-1941), distinguished French philosopher, author of *Creative Evolution* (1907), has made a contribution which has particularly interested biologists. While not bearing directly on the problem of the relation of mind and body, it has inclusive significance. Trained in mathematics and physics, Bergson was ambitious to understand the fundamental concepts of physics: time, space, matter, motion, force, energy. He decided that the time which enters into physical equations is not real time; that real time cannot be known by a measuring and standardizing intellect, but only by a direct perception of the passage of our inner life, which he later called intuition.

For Bergson this belief brought release from the shackles of naturalism and determinism, which he felt shut out real time and the real self; for the real self lives in the flow of time. Its states, he thought, are not strung along in causal succession, but they interpenetrate, carrying their past with them so that each one involves the whole self. The life of the self is thus not mechanically determined, because it meets each new experience with a new self and is therefore in its nature creative and evolving.

He felt that intuition could get behind the externalities of intellectual knowledge with its relativity, its abstract, static, analytical and partial features. He found intuition the exact counterpart of intellect in grasping wholes and getting immediate knowledge of the self and of continuity. He believed we can have direct knowledge of our own ego, even though the knower and the known are the same.

To Bergson life is not a derivative or product of physical nature, but a primary entity in the universe—the reality behind the material world and its activities. For him all life comes from a single source, *l'élan vital.* This vital impulse accounts for matter-energy at one end of the scale and for conscious mind at the other; but at times he seems to endow life with qualities usually credited to mind, such as inventiveness and memory.

In his *Time and Free Will,* Bergson shows that because life is creative, it is free and not mechanically determined as the mechanists think. Everything that has life in it is free in the sense that what it does from moment to moment *is a result* of its own spontaneous and novel inner activity and not of its surroundings—its tropisms and other necessities expressed in physical and chemical laws. This makes action unpredictable.

Bergson believed that *l'élan vital* may, as a rare and extreme achievement, be experienced by intuition as a central pulse of the life of the world in its unity. Intuition may stretch perception to a region beyond reach of our senses. It may perceive such invisible, intangible, imponderable, but nonetheless actual realities as life, time, space, mind and the self. This gift of poetic insight has lifted intuition to a position it had previously lacked. Bergson has added a real contribution to our conception of the creative nature of life and mind. Mind in action uses both intuition and intellect. The art of living wisely lies in keeping this working pair together.

Some have disposed of consciousness by asserting that it is a useless abstraction like "viscosity" and should therefore be ignored. Science cannot afford to ignore facts of experience. Can consciousness (mind) be considered useless when it is used in denying its usefulness? When Darwin disposed of purpose by the mechanism of natural selection, biologists saw in the terms "fitness to survive" and "adaptation to the environment" the *usefulness* of a structure or of a function as a sufficient reason for its existence. But "means-to-an-end" suggests a "cause-to-effect" process.

Another attempt to solve the mind-body problem regards the mind as an "epiphenomenon," an accompanying incident in a process which is assumed to have no causal relation to the further development of the process. This would make of mind a useless steam-whistle affair, an empty phrase, a subterfuge; which really amounts to saying that we can dispose of consciousness very easily by merely assuming that it does not require to be explained at all. To deny efficiency to mind, however, is to ignore the everyday, common-sense experience of its efficiency.

Mind, according to another view, is an *emergent* from a non-mental, *material* world. Mind, therefore, is a secondary phenomenon in a universe which is primarily non-mental. Mind, the theory is, emerged when material systems such as the bodies of organisms reached a high degree of organization and of chemical complexity. Some who hold this view of the origin of mind inconsistently consider mind to be a property or quality of the body. But properties or qualities of matter are passive, while consciousness or mind is synthetic and active, self-directive and creative. Sherrington says, "A reflex act must begin with a stimulus outside the body, but man's mind can will motor activity spontaneously, can even pursue pure contemplation (as in pondering a problem)." At that time his half-century of studying the human brain had proved for him that mental behavior is not entirely reflex and thus rooted ultimately in matter as Pavlov's disciples believe.

Some thinkers regard mind as a form of energy. All forms

of energy, however, involve motion in some direction and at some rate; they can be observed, measured, and tested. Thinking is in no sense a motion of any sort in any relation of space. Only figuratively do we ever speak of the direction and rapidity of thought. There are quanta of energy, but there are none yet known of thought. Consciousness is self-surveying, self-measuring and self-directing as no form of energy ever is.

Since the middle of the nineteenth century, there has been a growing acceptance of mind as a product of physico-chemical conditions of a highly evolved nervous system. Those who take this position list the following facts, largely based upon the relation of mental processes to brain physiology, to support their belief.

1. Sensations depend upon the integrity of special parts of the cerebral cortex. In other words, they have a physical basis.
2. The development of the mind is dependent upon the development of the brain.
3. Mental degeneration is correlated with that of the brain.
4. Consciousness is dependent upon blood supply.
5. Consciousness is lost under the influence of narcotics and becomes more active following the use of nerve stimulants.
6. Fatigue due to toxins in the blood affects the mind, memory especially.
7. There is a correlation between species of proportional brain-size and intelligence.
8. The mind is a composite effect (result) of the combined activity of the senses.

In connection with this last point, it is interesting to note that Sherrington says in *Man on His Nature,* "That the brain derives its mind additively from a cumulative mental property of the individual cells composing it has therefore no support from any facts in its cell structure." [21]

For some of us, all that the list proves is that mental processes may be *conditioned* by physiological processes. But since every event in the universe is conditioned, it would be most surprising if mental processes were not. The facts cited above suggest only that mental and physiological processes are distinguishable but correlated.

Another conception estimates mind and body as equally real and independent, although in man they form a temporary partnership which is dissolved by death. There is widespread and ever-recurrent belief that at death the body returns to the earth from which it came, while the soul persists in a spiritual universe free from the limitations of space-time and matter-energy. In our experience, mind is attached always to a living energy-system, through which it manifests itself to us and by means of which it receives communications from us. Will the forces of the universe, which have evolved both mind and its body, let mind perish when the body ceases to function and returns to primordial dust, or has mind its own kind of indestructibility? We shall deal with this problem later.

According to some idealists, the body is the *symbol* of the mind. As a part of nature, the body is a means of communication between minds, an important link. To Schopenhauer, the body is the external expression of the peculiarities of the will. He conceived of heredity as the will (mind) implementing itself. The body and its mind are inherited, but the mind gradually comes to dominate the body. As Kant says, "the mind knows its superiority to the body."

The assumptions of nuclear physics do not reveal what electrons, protons and neutrons are in reality. At least they do not prove that they are *non-psychical.* They may be like our ideas of them and, if so, psychical in reality. What except an idea is like an idea? "What is an electron or an atom but an idea?" asks the idealist. If the physical universe in the ultimate analysis consists of quanta of energy, this does not prove that the universe is in reality non-mental. May not energy be the way the mind expresses itself? *Matter* may be a symbol of mind.

Another solution of the mind-body relation would identify mental processes and brain changes as does Myers in his *Hobhouse Lectures* (1937). He admits that at first sight these most highly specialized forms of the two activities, respectively, conscious processes and the processes of living brain matter, "appear so different that it seems absurd to assert their identity. One feels like denying the possibility of any relation between them." But he concludes, "Mental activity and living bodily activity are identical." In *The Realm of Mind,* he asks, "Why, then, should we separate mental activity and cerebral activity, seeing that the two are identical?" [22]

Opposed to this, Sherrington in *Man on His Nature,* sees the brain as an "organ of liaison between energy and mind, but not as a converter of energy into mind or vice versa. . . ." This irreducible duality of energy and mind Sherrington calls *the biological dilemma.* "Mind in a sense is thus supernatural. . . . Mind, for anything perception can compass, goes in our spatial world more ghostly than a ghost. . . . Invisible, intangible, it is a thing not even of outline; it is not a 'thing.' It remains without sensual confirmation and remains without it forever. Stripped to nakedness there remains to it but itself. What then does that amount to? All that counts in life. Desire, zest, truth, love, knowledge, 'values,' and seeking metaphor to eke out expression, hell's depth and heaven's utmost height. . . . Mind yoked with life, how varied in its reaction! It will sit down and watch life acquiescent, or on the other hand, take life and squeeze it like an orange. . . .

"Between these two, naked mind and the perceived world, is there then nothing in common? Together they make up the sum total for us; they are all we have. We called them disparate and incommensurable. Are they then absolutely apart? Can they in no wise be linked together? They have this in common—we have already recognized it—they are both concepts; they both of them are parts of knowledge of one mind. They are thus therefore distinguished but not sundered: Nature in evolving us makes them two parts of the knowledge of one mind and that one mind our own. We are the tie between them. Perhaps we exist for that." [23]

Other critics of the identity position point out that things may be said about physiological changes in the brain which cannot be said about mental action. Neural processes always involve motion in some direction and at some rate. But an opinion, a judgment, memory and a solution of a problem—how little we know of their processes and causes! The best presentation I know of the contrasts between brain and mind is given by Hocking. I offer a condensed summary of it in case that stimulating text is not at hand.

a. The mind observes itself; the brain does not. . . .

b. The brain is in space; the mind is not. . . . But in whatever way the mind is related to space when space is thought of, it includes the whole of space in its view, and is therefore not "in" space. In this sense also, it is obviously far from being identical with the brain, which is one of the objects in space which we can think *about,* not think *with.*

c. The brain is in the present only: the mind is extended in time to the past and the future. . . . For the brain, the past is gone. Nothing can locate an image in the past except a mind which holds the past before it. And so with the future.

d. The brain is a set of facts: the mind is a set of facts and their *meanings.* . . . A fact *means* whatever it points to or leads to beyond itself. . . . What is a meaning for the mind is a connection for the brain. . . . But a connection is not a meaning. The physical fact, to itself, is meaningless. To the mind nothing is meaningless.

e. Among these meanings are qualities . . . and in particular, *pleasure* and *pain.* . . . The brain *per se* cannot enjoy nor suffer. The mind cannot escape joy and suffering; no experience is completely neutral. The mind is occupied with *values.* The brain is a system of facts.

In particular the mind is occupied with moral *values,* judgements of right and wrong. It is there, perhaps, that we feel the difference between brain and mind most sharply. . . . It is impossible for the sound human being to be morally neutral, just as it is impossible for him to ignore his sense of pleasure and pain. The brain is indifferent to right and wrong. To the mind this is the most important of distinctions.

These differences between the mind and that physical object we call the brain and nervous system, or the entire organism and its behavior, suggest at every point that the mind is something not only different from the body, but *more than* the body. They emphasize the query whether naturalism can explain the mind as a product of the body, the greater by the less.[24]

Whenever the body sets up its demands—instincts, hungers, complexes, needs—as deserving attention as separate realities, then we need to set a limit to its "rights" and take command as master, as a something more complete. That something more complete cannot be a life of the mind at odds with and apart from the body. It is a life of the mind which takes over and absorbs the body into its own currents of meaning, makes it mean what I mean instead of taking my directions from it.

In taking this position there is no question of how the mind brings its leverage to act upon the brain and body. Body and brain are not *another reality* such as could act on the mind or be acted on. *They are the mind,* its visible form, translated into the language of space and physical event. The mind as a part of nature is not acting on the brain as another natural object. The entire relation is consistently within the world of consciousness, for the mind is not identical with brain action, and really the mind is first and the brain-action derived from it. Idealists would say that the wills which are expressed in the world-phenomenon are acting on that mind and that the brain records the transaction in its own physiological language.

This is in agreement with what we usually feel about the

body. It is not identical with the self, but usable as a means of interchange with other minds. We say, "Here I am," as if it were equivalent to the self, as indeed it is because of the meanings which have been built into it by the self, making itself visible to other selves.

This does not imply that your individual mind produces its own body in the first place. The body comes to each of us, as does the rest of nature, from beyond himself. Each inherits his body as he inherits himself. But here also as in other experiences the mind is at first passive, then active; what it receives it can re-create. You can see that the body while less easily molded than imagination is much more easily molded than the rest of nature; it cannot resist the imprint of its owner's choices. This results in the fact that while at birth we have the body and the mind bequeathed to us, at middle age we have the body and the mind built by our own choices.

When electric power—the flow of electrons along a wire—swept in upon the electric revolution, the electron seemed wholly wire-bound and subject to strict physical and mechanical limitations! But later, on the basis of assumption, by isolating a stream of electrons in a high vacuum free from the bondage of wire, a new freedom and a new control were achieved. It is not unscientific to wonder if mind will ever achieve new freedom when freed by death from the *usefulness* and from the *bondage* of a living nervous system. Has mind a nature which, when freed from earth-born senses, may enter an existence with new sensitivenesses as it did at birth?

CHAPTER SIX

The Origin and Activities of Mind

With the convincing evidence that man's body has evolved from ancient origins, has come a belief that human mind also has evolved from simple beginnings of mind in lower animals. Perhaps it evolved from the awareness of benefit or injury, which Jennings, our foremost authority on protozoa, reports finding in all the one-celled forms he studied. This belief seems plausible since heredity can be traced in mental as well as in physical traits. The evolution of mind and body together may well be the basis of the unity that is such a striking attribute of the organization of complicated creatures which act as a unit instead of an aggregate of billions of self-centered cells, each doing its individual part in sustaining the life of the whole. But it throws no light upon the problem of the presence, the *origin* of consciousness in our world. There can be no doubt that mental capacities, once they are present in the animal series, have evolved together with the body. Darwin's *Origin of Species* and *Expressions of Emotions* (1872) offer important evidence for this fact. Later investigators—Romanes, Lloyd Morgan, Vervorn, Loeb and Yerkes—have ably stressed the inquiry concerning the point in the organic series at which we can assume that consciousness arises and what initial qualities it reveals.

The difficulties of such a line of work increase. The farther away we get from the human stage of mentality, the more the difficulties of such a line of work increase. If, however, mental life in human beings provides a significant clue to a directive factor in the universe, it is obviously important to understand the growth and development of mind wherever found.

Early students of the evolution of mind had no such accumulation of facts as the extensive literature of genetic psychology now furnishes. While this material varies in relevance to our problem of origin, it is true to the spirit of science in being selected to agree with no special viewpoint except that of experimentation. Such researches aid us in picturing the early stages of consciousness and the still speculative growth and development of the nervous system from its obscure beginnings to its present state of complicated dominance. They emphasize that the relation of consciousness to adaptive behavior is characteristic of more and more highly organized animals, and in human beings is both extended and implemented by language. All these facts increase the range of our scientific data but throw no light on the *origin* of mind in our universe. Is it a primary entity or a secondary reality *produced by* life as well as accompanying life?

Darwin in *The Descent of Man* (1871) summarized the evidence that mind as well as body has evolved, and concluded that, great as they are, the differences between mind in man and mind in the higher animals are differences of *degree,* not of kind. He believed that human mind had been derived from animal mind as the nervous systems had evolved with the rest of the body, determined by the same factors which had established all evolution. His arguments were accepted by many scientists but did not convince his friend Wallace, his co-discoverer of natural selection. Wallace maintained a position of what amounted to special creation for mind. He was unable to believe that "mere increase in chemical or physical complexity of matter could produce consciousness which cannot be explained by the laws and forces of matter but point clearly to the existence of an unseen universe to which the world of matter is altogether subordinate." He thought that similar new departures in the history of our world were shown by the appearance of matter, the appearance of life, the appearance of consciousness and then the appearance of the higher spiritual "faculties" of man. In his own words:

> On the hypothesis of this spiritual nature superadded to the animal nature in man, we are able to understand much that is otherwise mysterious or unintelligible in regard to him. . . . Thus we may perceive that the love of truth, the delight in beauty, the passion for justice and the thrill of exultation with which we hear of any act of courageous self-sacrifice are the workings within us of a higher nature which has not been developed by means of the struggle for material existence.

Herbert Spencer, who first used the term *evolution,* saw our problem much more clearly than either of the great pioneers, Darwin or Wallace. His active, vigorous mind gathered the scattered scientific findings of his day into a vast cumulative whole and grasped their bearing on the universal law of development through "differentiation and integration." Biology and chemistry would, he thought, solve the remaining puzzles, the gap between the living and the non-living, the chasm between mental and non-mental. He expected that the intricate processes of physiology would soon be understood through the steady extension of chemical laws, though the peculiar unification of processes in the organization of a complicated animal seemed to him beyond the possibilities of chemical action. The line between the mental and the non-mental caused him great perplexity. His inclination to regard consciousness as a form of energy was checked by the fact that mental energy did not admit of measurement (as did all other known forms of energy) in terms of the mass and velocity of moving particles. Nor could he find any evidence from the scientific procedures of his day that the physical energy of brain action declined when mental energy decreased; so he later considered consciousness an accompaniment of changes in the brain—rather an inexplicable accompaniment but one which we have to accept as being there. This, you can see, amounts to giving up the problem. He thought the mind might be a highly complex system of minute feelings "similar in nature to those we know as nervous shocks": but we are told he did not mean by this that a "nervous shock," which is a physical fact, is identical with a feeling, which is a mental fact. It still remained a mystery to him how the mental processes happen to accompany these nervous events. Mind was always turning up as an awkward *something else.*

Haeckel, early in the modern era, solves Spencer's problem in *The Riddle of the Universe* (1899) by use of the term *gradually.* "Consciousness," he says, "has been gradually evolved from the psychic reflex activity,"[25] reflex activity being, in his view, psychic but not conscious, a distinction that his critics think requires a certain agility to make. Haeckel's use of the word "riddle" implies that for him the solution was incomplete.

When Bergson published *Emergent Evolution,* its widespread acceptance had behind it the experimental procedures that had established the occurrence and permanence of mutations. No one yet knew their cause, so it was thought possible that life, mind, and reason might represent a series of steps of clearly distinguishable groups of phenomena. The older idea of evolution included the belief that all which unfolded must have been contained in the original "dust" or "shape." Emergent evolution, however, considers each new level an arrival to whose advent the whole configuration of events contributes. Without being any less a law-abiding universe, "gradually" is not its only method of action; it is capable of giving birth to novelty through mutations and thus in a sense to lifting itself upward. Whether this would have helped Spencer and Haeckel in overcoming the difficulties with which they struggled, we cannot know. Little was then known of the mechanisms of heredity. Chromosomes had not yet been observed, nor the assumption of genes adopted. The sudden appearance and permanent establishment of novelties known as "sports" had been observed but not explained. Genetics was later to become an active field of enthusiastic experimentation.

On the surface, it seemed to many that the new belief in emergence might explain the genesis of mind. But the earlier experimental work on mutations showed their occurrence too limited in range to encourage this belief. The radical differences in nature existing between matter-energy and consciousness or mind appeared to go deeper than mutations. At the same time, scientists realized that the nature of mind puts it beyond the reach of the methods of science. Its mechanism, the nervous system, is a perfect field for scientific investigation and experimentation, but the reality itself evades test tubes and measuring devices. Mind is imperceptible to our senses. With its quality of consciousness, its presence, however, is but rarely denied. Science is one of its most valued products.

To assert that consciousness is an "emergent" from nonmental sources can hardly be considered an explanation of its presence in the universe. Emergence might be the method of its appearance and evolution, but it does not explain its existence. Was it implicit in the beginning—implicit in the *process* of evolution rather than a product of the process? This would indicate mind as the very center of all that has evolved. It would place mind, not as having an animal origin, but as a primary reality in a living, evolving universe which was never without mind—whose very nature *is mind,* with evolution one of its expressions and its chief mechanism.

If mind has had an animal origin, it and its varied capacities have doubtless come from the first beginnings of awareness in the simplest animals, evolving through more and more complicated responses and through more and more complex response mechanisms. This would place mind as a physical product of a physical machine, a pure mechanism, when science is gravely questioning the basis of mechanistic concepts.

If we are not satisfied with the concept of the animal origin of mind, what other beliefs are offered? If we cannot accept the mechanistic concept presented, we have the alternative assumption that consciousness and mind, like matter-energy, are primary entities in the constitution of our universe, which is therefore a living minded universe and which always must have had the living quality of mentality and meaning.

Either view of the *origin* of mind is, of course, wholly speculative. But even if we so desire, it is impossible to avoid the problem presented by the *existence of consciousness*. It is only because we are conscious that there is a theory of evolution or a problem of any kind.

Those who first asserted the biological usefulness of mind were accused of the formulation of dogma, since scientific method could not prove, nor measure, nor corroborate. But there it was, a fact of experience, an objective reality. The biological utility of mind was a battleground between opposing forces. Lamarck had believed that mind led the way in organic evolution. This great Frenchman had put the "will to live" first among the factors in evolution. Most neo-Lamarckians had soft-pedalled the psychical element in Lamarckism because of their inability to reconcile it with the mechanistic interpretation of life. But Charles S. Minot had the courage of his convictions. In his presidential address before the American Association for the Advancement of Science (1902), he said,

> The development and improvement of consciousness has been the most important, really the dominant factor in the evolution of the animal series . . . if we thus assign to consciousness the leading role in animal evolution we must supplement our hypothesis by another, namely, that conscious actions are primary.[26]

From the standpoint of mechanism, the address was so unorthodox that one of his friends left it out of his bound volume of *Science* on the ground that it would undermine Minot's reputation as a scientist. It would never do to admit that consciousness can influence events in a physical universe. The controversy waged with high feeling and deep convictions but little proof. It was a question which did not lend itself to experiment.

But if consciousness can accomplish nothing, why could it evolve? Many could not accept Minot's belief that consciousness is primary, that without it the universe might come to absolute rest. Lamarckians maintained mind's usefulness, since otherwise it would have disappeared. Its continuance was proof enough of its utility (man's appendix, ear-moving muscles, etc. to the contrary, for useless organs are usually eliminated) so biologists were forced to hunt for some distinctive contribution which mind, however intangible, could make to life. Jacques Loeb, with his satisfaction in tropisms as explanations of most reactions, had to admit *educability* as a distinct contribution of mind to life. Psychology can dispose of many of the factors of education without using mind as a basis, but mind to many is the only entity which, irrespective of the nature of the stimuli, can explain response, not to facts alone but to their meanings. As a matter of survival it takes discernment to distinguish between hostile and friendly intentions, for the wolf is sometimes disguised in sheep's clothing. Only mind can discriminate between resembling stimuli when their meanings are so at variance. No robot, however cleverly devised, could do it. Also mechanisms have no suitable response ready for novel emergencies or conditions. Total situations appear to demand the use of mind to make trustworthy responses. Half a century later than Minot's assertion, the question is still unsettled. Theoretical questions in life-sciences have made little progress. Answers that lack proof are not convincing in science which is still often reluctant to admit metaphysics to its councils. But answers based on reason have accomplished great advances in physics and chemistry. Mind has kept on evolving. The evolution of learning has been impressive. The origin of mind is a theoretical question, still controversial.

Jennings, in his distinguished work on protozoa, found it difficult, if not impossible, to draw a line separating the activities of regulatory behavior of lower organisms from the so-called intelligent behavior of higher ones; "the one grades insensibly into the other." After exhaustive study of one-celled amoebae, he is "thoroughly convinced" that if they were large enough to come within our everyday experience, their behavior would indicate pleasure and pain, hunger, desire and the like on "precisely the same basis as we attribute these states to dogs." [27]

Much experimental work on the activities of mind has been done on conditioned responses and in making changes in habits. Such experiments have been used to show the differences among various kinds of animals in the number of trials required to establish a conditioned response. In one series it took a crayfish one hundred trials, a frog twenty, a dog five, and a human being one.

Ever since comparative psychology became a subject of laboratory experimentation with careful controls, a great many new facts have been discovered. Assuming that animal mind may be a subject of scientific study, the student of comparative psychology is confronted with two questions: How shall he get his facts, and how shall these facts be interpreted? It is now generally agreed that controlled experimental procedure must be his method and that standards of interpretation must be adopted.

By what criteria are we to determine whether or not an animal experiences emotions, perceives relations, reasons, is capable of volition? The difficulty is increased by the fact that psychological terms have been derived from human psychology, a circumstance which reinforces the natural tendency of students of animal behavior to *humanize* animals and to read into their behavior higher mental powers than they have. Lloyd Morgan suggested the use of a *canon,* or restraining principle. In comparative psychology the simpler the explanation the better. This may be misleading, but probably less so than would be the use of a more complex interpretation when a simpler one can be found.

Among types of activity, *tropisms* (from the Greek *tripo,* to turn) were claimed by Loeb and his followers to explain all movements, plant and animal alike. They are responses to gravity, light, contacts, chemicals, electricity, currents. They may be positive or negative, or either, at different times in the same individual. When a root grows down or a stem up, when leaves or stems turn toward the light or caterpillars go from or toward their "tents," or tendrils twist about an object, we have examples of tropisms. The plant does not choose to turn. It is forced to turn. Tropisms are not common in the animal kingdom. Applied to men and apes the theory is meaningless. Köhler's experiments on apes demonstrate that the ape responds not to a single external stimulus but to a general situation. Such experiments have done much to remove the "nickel in the slot" concept of animals from our minds.

Reflex action is a type of behavior manifested by animals with a nervous system. Early in the nineteenth century, the mind as an active affair was considered a phenomenon of stimulus and response. When a finger touches a hot iron, there is instant and mechanical withdrawal. The response takes that particular form because the nervous current is routed through the receptor-neuro-effector system along that inborn path of least resistance called a reflex arc. Reflex arcs may be combined; they may have ideas introduced into them; they may be controlled. When a drop of dilute acid is placed on the right side of a decerebrated frog, the right foot is raised as if to scratch away the irritant. If, however, the right foot is held, the left foot comes into action. The behavior is adapted to remove an irritant, but it is modifiable. Since, therefore, reflex action can be changed even when there is no brain, they cannot be regarded as simple mechanical actions. Reflex action is advantageous only under normal conditions of environment. Change the conditions, and the results are sometimes amusing. The normal orientation of the body of a crab is dependent upon the grains of sand which sink to the bottom of the otocyst (ear). If iron filings are substituted for the sand and a magnet is placed above the crab, the animal promptly turns over on its back. But even in the case of reflex actions, it has been discovered that different answers to the same stimulus may be given by the same animal, or by the same animal at different times. In most animals each stimulus causes, as a rule, not merely a single action that may be called a reflex, but, Jennings says, "a series of trial movements of the most diverse characters and including at times practically all of the movements of which the animal is capable." Typically, reflex actions involve only a part of the body, but they grade almost imperceptibly into *instinctive actions* which usually involve the entire body. Sherrington, in his Nobel Prize work on *The Integrative Action of the Nervous System,* writes,

> Certain it is that if we study the process by which in ourselves control over reflex action is acquired by an individual, *psychical* factors loom large, and more is known of them than of the purely physiological *modus operandi* involved in the attainment of the control.[28]

Instinctive behavior is a third type of behavior. Instincts are complicated sequences of behavior into whose composition a number of reflex arcs may combine. We are told that instincts modified by experience constitute our habits and thereby the character of each mature individual. This may seem too simple a scheme to account for memory or anticipation, for reasoning and all the higher mental processes, each of which is a matter for long and careful investigation. Instincts, according to Lloyd Morgan, are

> . . . complex coordinated motor responses to external stimuli performed without instructions and previous to experience in essentially the same way by all the members of the same species and sex and tending towards the well-being and preservation of the individual and the species.

While this definition applies to many instincts, it is not certain that it applies to all. In many instances, the impulse to action appears to come from within and not from without. It can hardly be an external impulse from South America which impels the young golden plover to launch out over the open sea when it flies from Nova Scotia southward. This is not a case of "homing," since the home is on the shore of Hudson's Bay. It is not a case of imitation, since the young birds lead the way. It has been suggested that the decrease in hours of daylight which limit the span of feeding time, so important for the young, may be an outside stimulus for migration to the south, but this is not established. A homing pigeon 500 miles from its roost, however, can hardly be stimulated from without at that distance. Evidence of guidance by magnetic currents is not yet demonstrated. The thought of its young and its mate might work as a stimulus from within. When McDougall discusses the instinct by which pigeons and bees find their way home under varying conditions of appearance, lighting, and odor, he infers that their behavior is guided not by any external stimuli acting on nerve machines but by a mind which has an idea of location and a purpose to get home. Much instinctive behavior, apparently, may be based upon internal "drives" and not directly determined by external stimulations.

Instinctive behavior is best illustrated by the behavior of *little-brained* types of animals like the insects, whose instincts are frequently very complex, generally inexplicable, and rarely modifiable by experience. They are machine-like in their perfection and inflexibility. Their dependence upon *organization* is evidenced by the change of instinct which follows metamorphosis, as from a caterpillar to an adult moth or butterfly. That instincts are inherited habits or *lapsed intelligence* seems highly improbable. All experimental evidence indicates habits are not inherited. The problem of the relation of the instinctive to the intelligent, conscious action remains unsolved.

In *big-brained* types of animals, instincts are modifiable through experience and hence may be considered to be not wholly unconscious. Machine-like as instincts appear, it seems impossible to describe or to interpret them in mechanistic terms, that is, in terms of chemistry and physics. One might know all about the physics and chemistry of a homing pigeon without knowing why the pigeon goes home or how it finds its way. Biology has its foundations in physics and chemistry, but a living organism is more and other than the sum of its parts. It seems a far cry from metabolism—i.e., bodily chemistry—to the homing of a pigeon.

Trial and error is a type of behavior often observed in all kinds of animals from protozoa to humans. The "avoiding" reaction of the slipper animalcule, Paramecium, is like "that of a blind and deaf person." The individual appears to be aware of what it is doing. "Most invertebrates," says Jennings, "perform many movements which have no fixed relation to sources of external stimuli, but which serve to test the surroundings and thus to guide the animals." They *select* from among the conditions encountered. Brief observation of an ant carrying food to its nest reveals no stimulations from without, but it does suggest a purpose from within. Put obstacles in its way, and it devises some method of getting around them. The food is not abandoned nor the direction permanently altered. Frustration is met by inventiveness and persistence.

Intelligent behavior in "big-brained" animals and human beings cannot be adequately interpreted without assuming that they are conscious, and that their consciousness makes a difference. We are dealing with intelligent behavior when instinctive responses are conditioned or controlled as a result of experience. Animals which are able to *profit by experience* we call *intelligent.* As an example of intelligent behavior may be cited that of a young chick which has eaten a wasp and been stung by it. The normal response to the sight of such an insect is the pecking instinct or reflex. When, however, the chick is stung, it drops the wasp and wipes its bill on the ground as if to get rid of a disagreeable sensation. Afterwards, if the chick is offered a wasp, it simply wipes its bill. "Never again!" This is not the way a machine behaves. Machines cannot learn anything; they do not change their behavior as the result of experience. So far as animals are tropistic, or reflex, or instinctive in their actions, if they are conscious, the consciousness appears to make no difference.

But in intelligent behavior, consciousness acts as an efficient factor. Something from the past is carried over into the present. Whether this implies a mind which contrasts past and present, or whether it is wholly due to the traces left in nerve centers that change reactions, is controversial. Let us keep such significant divergence of opinion in mind to give point to each bit of evidence life brings to view.

Trial and error and profiting by experience both belong in the general category of learning. Educational methods have been greatly clarified by the modern concept of the importance of training by well-defined methods of clear presentation. The advantages of these methods of training are obvious in all attempts to train animals. If they have minds, it is perfectly fair to assume that they are like human minds, to some degree. If they were qualitatively different, they would be quite unknowable. To know mind in animals it seems best to study mind in those animals which physically resemble man most closely, that is, in great apes. Fortunately, through the efforts of such well-trained experimentalists as Köhler and Yerkes, we are in possession of a mass of well-attested evidence that these animals have minds. Apes respond to tactual, visual, auditory, gustatory and olfactory stimuli much as we do. With similar sensoria there is little doubt that their sensations resemble ours. Similar psychological conditions may be assumed to be correlated with similar mental processes.

But the inference that apes have minds is justified by more convincing evidence than this. Apes learn, and learn quickly. Like children, they can be taught to dress and undress themselves, to eat with a spoon, to know their names, to come when called, to copy letters on a blackboard, and to do many other things which only a conscious individual is known to do. Since they have senses like our own, they unquestionably have sensory experiences like ours. Their educability shows that they are capable of associating one experience with another. Many of Köhler's experiments with chimpanzees demonstrate that such association frequently occurs. For example, he hung bananas where the apes could get them only by means of a swinging rope. After they had learned to get the bananas in this way, they would begin swinging the ropes as soon as Köhler appeared with the bananas in his pocket. Through association they anticipated what was about to happen.

As to the emotional life of apes, all observers agree that it closely resembles that of human beings. Köhler writes that it is

> . . . hardly an exaggeration to say that a chimpanzee kept in solitude is not a real chimpanzee at all. The first and greatest desire of the separated creature is to get back to the group. Very young ones are extremely frightened and show their fear to such a degree that one simply has not the heart to keep them apart any longer.[29]

Older animals in solitary confinement lose their appetites and refuse to eat. According to Köhler, apes show sympathy, affection, rage, sadness, excitement, distress, grief, awe, pity, hate, joy, jealousy, coquetry, dislike, and sexual excitement. In view of this similarity in emotional life, it is not surprising that Yerkes characterizes apes as "almost human."

Köhler states that the

> . . . register of emotional expression (in apes) is much greater than that of the average person, because his whole body is agitated and not merely his facial muscles. He jumps up and down in joyful anticipation and impatient annoyance and anger; and in extreme despair, which develops under very slight provocation, he flings himself on his back and rolls wildly to and fro.[30]

He also swings and waves his arms about his head in a fantastic manner, as an expression of disappointment and dejection.

That animals, even apes, deliberately try to recall something which has been forgotten, has not been demonstrated. Of course, some animals do remember for months, but that probably involves associative processes only, and not the active attempt of the animal to recall something. Köhler thinks that some of his apes exhibit memory when, after a night's sleep, they go straight to the spot where they had seen fruit buried the day before; but the evidence that the mind of the ape is active in this case is not convincing.

Since animals lack symbols (words) which express relations, Lloyd Morgan doubted that they focus relations at all. Logical relations involving a high level of abstraction are probably beyond them. But there is evidence that they focus practical relations. When the ape Sultan, in order to reach a banana, lengthened his bamboo pole by putting a smaller one into a hole at the end of a larger one, perception of the spatial relations appears to have been involved in the act. When an ape uses three or four boxes to enable him to reach a hanging banana, does it not seem possible that there is focusing of spatial relations? Of course, if word symbols are needed for the mind to focus relations, apes have no such tools. But it has not been shown that symbols to express relations are necessary in order that they may be focused. Nevertheless, Lloyd Morgan's skepticism of the capacity of animals to do this is probably justified. At present, the question may be considered an open one.

Much has been said about *reason* in animals. That animals do reason is affirmed by some comparative psychologists and is denied by others. Such differences of opinion are largely due to different definitions of the term. According to Lloyd Morgan, an animal, in order to reason, must ask the question, "wherefore?" and answer it by a "therefore." In order to raise and answer such a question, an animal would have to take an interest in the *why* of the causal relations, not merely their existence. Since there is no evidence that an animal does any such thing, and even if he did, that he would have the vocabulary required, Lloyd Morgan denied reason in animals. For that matter, there are plenty of human beings who probably never reason in this abstract manner. Reasoning is a most important factor in the development of adaptive behavior in human beings. Through it we can anticipate events and get ready for them. Psychologists suggest that we often supplement rational thinking with random thinking which helps us to picture how we would act in imaginary circumstances. This, they say, is the method we use in science when we work with hypotheses. A large number of supposed cases of reasoning in animals are found, on critical examination, to be instances of association and must therefore be discarded as irrelevant.

According to other psychologists, reason is manifested

whenever an animal *adapts a means to an end.* When the ape Sultan lengthened the pole by joining two short ones in order to reach a banana, we had an instance of this sort of practical reasoning. The construction of a four-storied tier of boxes by the ape Grande, in order to reach the suspended banana, is another example of the same sort of psychology. The ape Chica, who combined the use of a tier of boxes and a pole in order to reach food, may also be credited with reasoning in this sense.

Yerkes tells us in *Chimpanzees* (1943):

> Meanings and values determine the scope and quality of an organism's adaptive and constructive life; this is true of chimpanzees and men. In both, hereditary, that is, structurally established, meanings abound, and in both there is also large and varied capacity for the acquirement of new meanings through racial tradition and individual experience with animate and inanimate social and non-social environment.[31]

To such studies we look hopefully when in search of origins and early phases of evolutionary and developmental progress of the human mind.

One of these *hereditary and structurally established meanings* may be seen in the development of our eyes, a ballast of fact for any speculation we may have in our thinking about the relation of structures in organisms to cosmic conditions. The human eye, developing in pre-natal darkness, prepares a refinement of structure to work in the medium of light which shows a relation of the structure to the atomic character of the properties of light which we cannot ascribe to a *chance* relationship. It may indicate activity of mind of cosmic grasp—world mind. I quote from an address given before an International Congress on Light Therapy in 1932 by Nils Bohr, 1922 Nobel Prize winner in the field of quantum theory, and the man who laid the foundation of modern atomic theory:

> . . . opthalmology has revealed to us the ideal properties of the human eye as an optical instrument. Indeed, the dimensions of the interference patterns, which on account of the wave nature of light set the limit for the image formation in the eye, practically coincide with the size of such partitions of the retina which have separate nervous connection with the brain. Moreover, since the absorption of a few light quanta, or perhaps of a single light quantum (this latter has recently been proved by Hecht at Columbia), on such a retinal partition is sufficient to produce a sight impression, the sensitiveness of the eye may even be said to have reached the limit imposed by the atomic character of the light effects. In both respects, the efficiency of the eye is the same as that of a good telescope or microscope, connected with a suitable amplifier so as to make the individual processes observable . . . owing to the very limits imposed by the properties of light, no instrument is imaginable which is more efficient for its purpose than the eye. Now this ideal refinement of the eye, fully recognized only through the recent development of physics, suggests that other organs also, whether they serve for the reception of impression or not, will exhibit a similar adaptation to their purpose, and that also in these cases the feature of individuality symbolized by the quantum of action, together with some amplifying mechanism, is of decisive importance. That it has not yet been possible to trace the limit in organs other than the eye, depends solely upon the simplicity of light as compared with other physical phenomena.[32]

How little we know of the forces that fit developing structures in organisms for their future uses! The human eye with its essential structure, a light-sensitive screen at its back, made up of about 137 million separate seeing elements spread out in the sheet of the retina, each with nerve connections in the brain, is an amazing structure! A pair of these perfected spheroid cameras are adjusted so the mind can read their two pictures as one. Self-turning, self-focusing by automatically changing the shape of the lens for near or far, they clean their delicate, glass-clear surfaces by automatic action of soft, moist-lined, protective lids and bathe them with tear-water which is able to destroy germs which might inflame their surfaces. These cameras register a continuous moving picture throughout every waking hour of life. Without changing film, they receive, take and record whatever pictures present themselves or are chosen, signaling their shifting exposures to the brain. Such perfection suggests an activity of mind, a plan, or a purpose which cannot be dealt with by science.

When Bergson found that certain rapidly moving mollusks such as octopus and squid had, by stages in the course of evolution, produced eyes astonishingly like the eyes of the unrelated group of vertebrates, he inferred that the two series had been guided by a common vital impulse to respond to the conditioning of light. Is there such guidance?

There is in animals a great variety of photo-receptors. Those of vertebrates work in the same way as those in active mollusks, but they do not develop and did not evolve in the same way. In the vertebrate eye the sensory cells are aimed away from the light, and in mollusks they are aimed toward it. In each case the response to the cosmic conditions of light works upon the uses and structures which present themselves in different series. There is evidently some reality of cosmic influence as well as some factor of what Sherrington calls *foreknowledge* enabling cells to select the materials and build the structures needed for future work under conditions not yet experienced. We know of nerve connections, the distribution by the blood of stimulating hormones, and the appearance of enzymes in each cell which determine certain kinds of growth, but these are all part of an integrated working to a pattern which still has to be explained. Is there in organisms, some directive, psychic mental factor imperceptible to sense, or is it pure chemistry, physics and quantum mechanics?

Just what is it that mind does for an organism which the body with its nerves and brain cannot do? Are there factors in the types of behavior we have observed and in the phases of evolution we have considered which cannot be explained by the resources of chemistry and mechanics? McDougall in *Outline of Psychology* states that the most fundamental function of mind is to guide bodily movement so as to change our relation to objects about us. Such guidance may be purely reflex, but when ideas are introduced by degrees into the reflex arc, the working of an adult mind may become infinitely complex, as in some types of behavior, such as conducting a symphony orchestra, performing a delicate surgical operation, or teaching complicated subjects to advanced students.

When we watch the natural behavior of animals, they seem to be "running themselves." Their actions make us feel that we can understand what they are "up to," what they are trying to do. A machine never *tries* to do anything. It must move to the purpose of an operator or to the purpose of the maker of its "works." Lotze's mechanical beetle never falls off the table, not because it is intelligent, but because the inventor of its mechanism is. There are many kinds of self-regulating machines, self-guiding, self-equilibrating, self-stopping, and so on. A great power-loom stops instantly when one of its threads breaks, and it remains stopped until an attendant mends the thread and starts the machine. Animals, however, when interrupted in what they are doing, find some way of continuing. They show inventiveness and persistence in overcoming obstacles, and they adjust themselves flexibly to new situations as no mere mechanism could. They are also capable of keeping an end in view. When we watch them, they seem to behave intelligently. Is anything but mind intelligent?

There is no doubt that the receptor-neuro-effector system operates by mechanical means, as does an automobile. But like the auto, however wonderful and efficient its engine, it requires an operator, a driver whose judgment puts the mechanism at the service of special tasks and definite purposes. Such purposes in both man and animals may include the urge to live and the activities whereby each lives. Both these lines of activity may be mechanical, but not all adult human mental activities are wholly mechanical.

The special utility of human mind seems to lie in the ideas which are introduced into reflex arcs. Mind guides action in judging which of many possible responses is in keeping with the permanent values of the individual. If all my past experiences are registered in my brain, it is my mind alone that can survey them and choose a response which will mean what *I* mean, a line of action characteristic of *me*. It is myself alone, my *mental* self, that can choose what *I* prefer to do. Judgment and choice are mental activities. An intelligent reaction to a novel situation needs *mind*, which alone can grasp the *meaning* and *significance* of facts as well as the bare facts themselves.

The need to understand this point of view is important at a time when for various reasons science is frankly outgrowing its devotion to mechanism. Life and mind have always been difficult to bring completely within the bounds of mechanism because of the presence of consciousness and its inaccessibility to our senses. Further, it has become hard to devise types of mechanisms which could account for observed facts of physical phenomena; and to this has been added a conviction that the mechanical elements of a phenomenon are partly a result of our mechanical observations and do not represent the whole of nature. Moreover, many new phenomena, revealed by applications of quantum theory and relativity, simply cannot be explained in terms of the classical behavior of machines.

The problem of the origin and establishment of nature's mechanisms has supplanted, in its challenge to thinking, the problem of evolution. It seems a more important problem because it is deeper and inclusive. It more definitely demands cooperation with philosophy's close reasoning as a basis for reaching truth. What is behind the great mechanisms of the universe, the perfection with which they work together, the laws under which they operate? Laws are considered a manifestation of intelligence.

Behind all man-made mechanisms is the obvious activity of human mind. Whether the mechanisms are atomic bombs or automobiles, barrel organs or bicycles, electric lights or egg-beaters, each is the result of thinking; a triumph of thought over things, a mastery of mind over matter.

The ever-increasing mass of man's mechanisms may be considered as evidence of the ascendancy of mind and its educability in the evolution of man, not as something added but as something basic in all being, ready to evolve as it becomes freed, implemented and directed.

If we accept the activity of human mind as behind all man-made mechanisms, it may be possible to believe that something of the nature of mind on a cosmic scale is the source of all mind, that world-mind is behind the great mechanisms of the universe, the expanding galaxies, the varied but calculable motions of our solar system, its sources of light and heat, the photosynthesis of plants, the structure and organization of living cells, and of atoms. The repeatable performance of the development of the human embryo, each with its unique heritage of genes but each with all the range and detail of its race, is the result of many mechanisms.

We all recognize man as a physicochemical system. But we see him as a complex individual pattern against a background of a complicated cosmic pattern. There he takes his place as a psychophysical system. He alone, among all the products of evolution, has a mind which questions the process, sees himself in relation to it, sets out to prove and to explain it, to understand its mechanisms, and to control evolution. He becomes a thinker, exploring the evidences of mentality in his cosmos, wondering if it, like himself, is living and minded.

If there is a psychic factor in living systems, directing their growth and development, biology must devise some way of dealing with it even if it is inaccessible to our senses. Physics had accepted realities imperceptible to our senses, long before the assumption could be proved.

To admit a psychic, directive factor in the growth and development of organisms is not to say that the cells are conscious of their specific selectivity. When you select a record for your phonograph to give you a repeatable performance of a beautiful song, you have no thought that the record and the machine which delivers it so faithfully are conscious of their performance. Yet consciousnesss and mind are built into the invention and construction of both the phonograph and the record as they are also built into the work of the composer and the artistry of the singer who interprets his music.

Is the assumption that such a relationship of mind to organisms and to their mechanisms may be the result of a minded universe more difficult to accept than the assumption that they result from mindless reactions of chemistry and mechanics in a universe without mind?

Whatever our belief about the place of mind in the universe and its relation to living systems, it must be based on an assumption, since there are no observable facts. But assumptions are not unscientific. They serve as tentative solutions of questions for which science has no answers. Is the assumption of a minded universe a belief that makes sense of the facts before us?

We can all accept the belief that the human being is *one* reality, but for some of us, whether that one is primarily the body or primarily the mind is not so easily decided. Beliefs about reality are metaphysical in their nature. The implications of the measure and the meaning of mind in the human individual and in the universe are always in process of revision. They shift with changes in our sense of the intelligibility of the universe. To some they spell finality, to others they add the vistas of eternity. Thomas Huxley once soberly remarked:

> The longer I live, the clearer it is to me that the most sacred act of a man's life is to say and to feel "I believe thus and so to be true." All the heaviest rewards and all the greatest penalties of existence cling about that act.

Can you think of mind with its entire range of discriminative, reflective, intelligent, rational integrative and creative capacities, its conflicts as well as its unities, at the center and source of all that makes up your world? Whether you call it *God's mind, world-mind, cosmic-mind, creative spirit,* or *nature,* its contribution to the world and its life are the same. In the beginning was mind! Mind is incarnated in the nature and law-abidingness of all matter-energy, embodied in all the facts of sense, implicit in the nature of life and all its activities, inherent in the processes of all evolution, basic in all nature.

It may add clarity to your thought of the intelligibility of the universe to think of mind as the creative force at the core of the universe, working itself out through all the mechanisms with their processes and forces which it has created and established and used.

As we have come to think of human life as a continuation of the larger cosmic evolutionary process, not as an exception to the rest of the universe, so we may, perhaps, come to think of human mind as a continuation of limitless and ordered mind at the source of the universe with life itself as a cosmic mechanism for the evolution, individuation and perfection of mind.

CHAPTER SEVEN

Philosophy, Reality, Purpose

Philosophy deals with our beliefs about the world as a whole. This includes ourselves and the universe about us—the total of all our experiences. It is the report the human mind gives to itself about the constitution of the world and of mankind and their interrelations.

No branch of science has anything to say about the world as a whole, even astronomy, which always leaves out the astronomer. Each science has its own field. Neither singly, nor together, do they make up a philosophy. No type of philosophy questions the truth of science; all philosophies have deep interest in science and the implications of its findings. No scientist, as such, would make a judgment of the non-existence of anything outside his own field, nor would they collectively state that all realities are covered by their studies.

Your philosophy is what you believe. It includes all your

beliefs of widest range and deepest significance that enter into religious creeds, political principles, standards of right and wrong, your general scientific beliefs. Its questions are those which come to any thoughtful mind as it inquires into the nature of experience and the meaning of life. Are there proofs of the existence of God? What is His nature? Is He concerned with persons? Is death man's end? Are men born free and equal? Should one race be subject to another? Is a world government possible? Are right and wrong absolute or relative? Is moral law real? What gives it validity? Are we morally responsible? Are our wills free? Is natural law the result of intelligence or chance? Are there realities beyond reach of the senses? Is human behavior part of the machinery of nature? What is the make-up and structure of our universe?

These are the great concerns and issues in human life. Answers to many of them lie beyond our experience, yet we include them in our beliefs. How did that come about? How did they become part of our philosophy?

If you examine the sources of your beliefs, you trace them variously to tradition, authority, education, experience, intuition, superstition, prejudice, imitation, or some other influence. Your collection may seem too motley a lot to be dignified by the term *philosophy,* and you yourself too undeserving of the name *philosopher*—lover of wisdom. Yet the creative activity of adopting beliefs and putting them together goes on unencouraged. The compelling urge to wonder and to ask "What is it all about?" makes us believe that man *must philosophize* whatever his intelligence or training. It is an inevitable activity for a thinking being.

Philosophy does not say that you have no right to believe

what you cannot prove. It does not insist that every belief must be based on reason. To quote Hocking:

> What it does is to inquire what the grounds are on which beliefs are held and what grounds are good grounds. It may find a place for prejudice, distinguishing justifiable from unjustifiable prejudice. It may in some cases sanction authority as a ground for belief, aiding us to discriminate between a good authority and a bad one. It may advise us in other cases to rely on intuition, offering some way of telling a true intuition from a false one. A large part of its business is to inquire what reason can do and what it cannot do in the way of supporting belief . . . so long as false beliefs are possible, and such false beliefs in vital matters are perilous luxuries, there can be no virtue in declining to think about the foundations of belief. The idea that philosophy is presumptuous can only mean that it is too ambitious a thing to try living intelligently in so vast a universe; and that it is somehow more modest to go it blind! Surely it is extravagant to imagine that the capacity for thinking is an inherent vice. We cannot, even if we would, prevent ourselves from thinking about the frame and principles and destiny of our lives; and we believe that the right use of reason brings us nearer truth, not further away from it. Thus philosophy itself may be said to be founded upon a belief, a belief expressed long ago by Socrates, "that the unexamined life is not worth living by a man." [33]

Philosophy, in seeking to understand our world and human life, assumes that they are intelligible. It concerns itself with reality, with the meaning of life and with the art of living. Most philosophies end in belief in God—but an intellectual belief in God must not be confused with religion. There are many variations and types. Be prepared for differences of opinion and lack of agreement. Meet these as a challenge to do your own thinking. How can you expect a simple and easy account of anything so complex as our universe and the lives of human beings? Such differences may help us to discover *universals* and the changelessness of those factors in which certainties are rooted. We may well wonder if there is any one belief about our world which in broad and simple outline we can call a sure possession of the human race.

The formulation of a personal philosophy is a lifelong enterprise; like life itself, it is living, growing, changing, striving toward consistency and cohesiveness. You wish it to be "all of a piece" and to agree with your cumulative experience of reality.

The value of your philosophy will be measured largely by your desire to give yourself a reasonable account of your world and what you are doing in it. Is it a world of law and significance? What does human experience mean and imply? You philosophize when you critically examine such questions honestly and persistently.

Whatever your beliefs, they are your outfit for managing a life, the tools for shaping its destiny and meaning. Whether acquired intentionally or unintentionally, your philosophy is your ground for decisions, your basis of action.

For its facts about the constitution of the physical universe, philosophy turns to science. Science has built up a great respect for facts and for the justice due to them. Facts are known through reports of the senses; they can be shared by competent observers and proved by sensory verification. Science starts with a problem, gathers evidence first-hand, sorts the facts discovered, and then attempts to generalize or, rarely, to explain the facts. Thus science is based upon experiences which may be shared by qualified witnesses. It describes, classifies, generalizes, and occasionally explains. It asks, What? How? When? Where? and doubtfully, Why? Science seeks to interpret physical events as far as possible in terms of physics and chemistry, i.e., in mechanistic terms. Science experiments and reports its results. It does not try to interpret these in terms of meaning or of value; it is a *methodology,* with self-imposed limitations of aim.

Science has also been busy in extending and amplifying the reach of human sense organs through microscopes, telescopes, spectroscopes, oscilloscopes, electroscopes, through telephones, microphones, cloud chambers, and many electronic devices. With the demands upon our minds to grasp great distances and large numbers, has come great satisfaction in dealing also with the very small. Man can now measure time in thousandths of a second and temperatures in hundred-thousandths of a degree. He has made a galvometer which can measure a millionth of an ampere of electric current, equaling 6 billion electrons a second. A recent electrometer measures nearly a millionth of this amount. These all give evidence of many realities beyond reach of unaided sense organs. Their success has helped build up a belief that all realities will eventually be revealed to sense perception and proved by sensory verification. When, however, in nuclear physics the study of radiation had reached the limits of traceable causation, the physicists took a leap into the imperceptible and *assumed* a hypothetical structure for atoms with electrons whirling about a nucleus of protons and neutrons. As we have noted before, this assumption *worked* as an explanation of the known phenomena long before experiments with cloud chambers proved it true. So science at times uses methods of reaching knowledge which it cannot immediately prove. *Meta*physics, a branch of philosophy, *beyond* physics, accepts assumptions, logic and reasoning as reliable paths to truth. It realizes with Hobbes as does science, "It is obvious that truth and falsehood dwell only with those living creatures who have the use of speech" and are therefore careful to explain their beliefs in words of definite meaning.

Philosophy has two methods of work. It analyzes before it synthesizes. It looks into our sources of belief as does science; questions the nature of thought, its relation to reality; examines the status and destiny of consciousness; asks what is truth and how to reach it; inquires if there are realities beyond reach of the senses; studies the laws of logic and consistency; criticizes all implications and assumptions; measures the limitation of reasoning; examines every approach to knowledge. Its chief concern is the meaning of all these activities.

Philosophy's second method is synthesis, the putting together of tested knowledge. This is its chief contribution to human thought. In this highly practical work, philosophy examines critically its sources, making sure they are recognized for what they are. Its aim is to reach a meaningful whole, *a* philosophy, a world-view, which shall omit nothing in the ceaseless, life-long stream of experience, yet be an ordered, integrated reality.

When the human spirit in its climaxes of experience

cries, "Why? Oh why?" it is searching for meaning. The minds which desire to interpret, to understand, to grasp meanings, to know the realities behind appearance, feel the need of something beyond the analytical method of science. The synthetic method of philosophy offers this different approach. As Driesch said, "Science without philosophy is blind; philosophy without science is empty." Thus philosophy differs from the special sciences in its range. Each science deals with a portion of the field of knowledge; philososphy attempts to frame a picture of the whole, to establish a world-view. In his *First Principles,* Herbert Spencer proposed to define science as partially unified knowledge; philosophy as completely unified knowledge. The problem of reality requires this metaphysical approach. To confuse a methodology with a metaphysic is a serious error. Thomas Huxley helped us to avoid this when he wrote:

> But the man of science who, forgetting the limits of philosophical inquiry, slides from materialistic formulae and symbols into what is commonly understood by materialism, seems to me to place himself on a level with the mathematician who should mistake the x's and y's with which he solves his problems for real entities—and with this further disadvantage, as compared with the mathematician; that the blunders of the latter are of no practical consequence; while the errors of systematic materialism may paralyze the energies and destroy the beauty of a life.

Philosophy deals with realities; but how do we judge what is real? Are there degrees of reality, some entities more real than others? Is there a *real* as distinct from the phenomenal? Are our eyes and ears distorting organs, giving us the richness of color from wave lengths of colorless light and the moving power of music from vibrations of soundless air? If color and sound come only from the impact of light waves and air vibrations on our conscious minds, are both the mental experience and the physical phenomena equally real? Is the sensation *red* which we experience any more real than the special wave lengths that bring us that sensation? Such waves themselves remain totally outside our conscious experience except through experiments in a laboratory. Waves bring the vibrations; our minds supply the color and sound. Eddington says:

> We do not pluck out our eyes because they persist in deluding us with fanciful colorings instead of giving us the plain truth about wave lengths. It is in the midst of such misrepresentation of environment (if we may call it so) that we have to live. It is however, a very one-sided view of the truth which can find in the glorious coloring of our surroundings nothing but misrepresentation—which takes the environment to be all important and the conscious spirit to be inessential.[34]

Most of us commonly accept two kinds of realities as true; first, physical objects such as stars and cars, and second, states of mind such as pleasure and pain. The history of human thought has varied as it has because to some men the physical fact is the impressive and sufficient type of reality. They believe we must explain mental realities from it. To them mind is a derivative of physical reality. They tend toward the type of philosophy called naturalism. To others, mental reality, the feeling or the mind seems more real. They maintain that physical realities are known only through mind and that therefore our knowledge of nature is mental, however real nature itself may be. They tend toward *idealism.* When such opposing beliefs cannot be reconciled, a choice must be made. Neither position can be proved nor disproved but, as we have noted, failure to prove a position does not disprove it. You will do well if you can decide which view is more in harmony with your basic beliefs.

The Nature of Reality is philosophy's basic question. Is the base, the cause, the condition of human experience physical and material as naturalists hold? Is it mental and spiritual as idealists believe? Or is it both, as the dualists think? Or may it be plural? On this matter we meet fundamental opposition of views. When each position has adherents and advocates, how can one choose? It is a far-reaching decison whether we think of the world as indifferent matter or as living mind, whose lasting, durable factors both think and plan.

During the long course of evolution, living creatures have continually needed to distinguish between reality and the semblance of reality—the mirages of the world. Not only have higher animals concealed their real intentions, but men have cloaked greed and malice unrecognizably and used the power which hypocrisy easily gives.

Nature herself presents many an appearance different from reality: moonrise, sunset, the daily journey of the sun from the east to the west, the seeming fixity of our earth which we have to be told is rushing through space and revolving; the stable solidity of the common objects we use each day, which are revealed by science to be made up of whirling energy systems with proportionately vast spaces between these systems; the three-dimensional experience from the flat surface of a photograph or projected film; the seeming break in an oar or a spoon where it enters the surface of water. It is an important part of human life to judge between appearances and the true state of affairs, to know shams and realities for what they are, to distinguish the show world from the real one.

Science has been busy exploring both these worlds, making an end of superstitions by revealing new mysteries and disclosing a deep order and intricacy in nature. It passes no verdict on the structure of our universe, not because it does not care, but because the decision whether the basis of human experience is material or mental is beyond its method. Science is busy learning new facts and their relations, which can be shared or verified. Philosophy accepts all the facts of science but feels that facts about realities do not reveal their full essence. Their reality is what they mean. Reality, then, is the kind of experience which maintains itself in all later judgments. This self-maintenance convinces us of reality; it's a quality that corrects our illusions. If physical realities are external to us, they are not external to our minds. They become qualities of our experience and are therefore not outside it. Experience involves knowing a reality which is not ourselves. When we learn by experience, we feel that it is reality that teaches us. Experience does come in to us from outside. If reality is mental, however, it must be some other mind at work upon us. The real question, then, is the nature of this outside active reality. Is it physical? Is it mental? Idealists call it world-mind. Can you think of world-mind as a reality?

In science the principle of causality is a basic assumption that nothing occurs without a sufficient cause. It assumes that every event in the universe is governed by the cause and effect relation. Is physical causation real? Before proceeding to search for the relation of reality to philosophy, can we decide: Is causality a reality which applies to consciousness and mind? Are human minds cause and effect affairs?

In ordinary experience, we think of the cause of an event as some other event which immediately precedes the given event and seemingly requires it to be. Causes precede and seem to push their effects into being. We turn a key to switch on the ignition; we press a button, and the engine starts. There is no question in our minds about the cause and the effect and the relation of the two. We might describe causality as the determining of events from behind in time. But when we start the car, we have a purpose, a desire to get to another place—a future state of being somewhere else, which we wish to bring about. Here purpose determines events from ahead in time. Is it possible that all physical events lie in some causal series, while all mental events lie in some purposive sequence? All normal human beings have desires, choices, preferences and the disposition to act so as to bring these to fulfillment. Are the two processes complementary, as Aristotle thought, or mutually exclusive?

When I hear my neighbor's lawn mower, I am sure that the mind which invented that machine worked to a purpose. The man, too, who pushes it is not wholly a part of its mechanism. He has a purpose, a future state of his lawn which, with the help of the machine, he can bring to pass.

His action may be the immediate *cause* of the mowing, the noise, and the work of the machine; but his whole undertaking has *a purpose,* which, to my mind, cannot be excluded by the consistencies of technical causal psychology nor by mechanism. Purpose is a fact of experience, and it has found some way of getting along with the causes. Indeed, wherever there is consciousness, purpose seems to flow along with the causal stream.

Causal action is always inferred. It cannot be observed. We do not see it working. We may have no *proof* of causal relation even when we have a convincing sequence of events. The blow hits: a man falls; we do not see the force in the blow of the fist. A moving picture would give us an equally real sensation with no force involved.

If causation cannot be observed, why do we feel so sure about causal laws? We *believe* every event has a cause and are led by this belief to try to fit events together. How have we come to believe that every event must have a cause? Hume thought it resulted from mental habit—when we observe often and without exception that x follows y, we expect every x to be followed by y. When this is confirmed repeatedly in a great variety of instances of sequence, we easily adopt a belief that for every event a cause can be found. The real force of our belief in causality, Hume thinks, lies in the strength of our expectation. It is, then, only probable, not certain, that every event has a cause. We have no proof. Kant found it difficult to justify what was called the "causal axiom," that every event must have a cause and a sufficient one. He thought it a product but a necessary product of our way of knowing. If there is causality in the world-order, it is imputed, not seen.

Some modern physicists would do away with the idea of physical causation on the ground that it is not needed in the description of physical events. They deny the influence of one thing on another and consider the idea of necessary connection between cause and effect as metaphysical. However, even if physicists do not need the idea of causality in the description of the supersensible elements of theoretical physics, it does not follow that it is useless in the description of events in the world revealed to the senses. We must admit that causal connection is an immediate datum of experience. Causal relations, as invariable sequences which occur under similar conditions, have as good foundations in experience as have logical relations.

Purposes, like causes, cannot be observed. They too are imputed. I hear the driver of a passing car begin to honk its horn lightly but persistently while the car slows down and draws up to the curb ahead. Since I am the only visible pedestrian, I hasten toward the waiting car. It is wholly conjecture on my part that a friend has recognized me and has stopped to offer me a lift, but such proves to be the case.

As we can neither prove nor disprove that every event has a cause, so also we can neither prove nor disprove that every event has a purpose. Failure to find either does not disprove its existence. It is logically possible that every event has *both a cause and a purpose* or meaning.

Purpose as a cause of events has been objectionable to scientists ever since Descartes in his *Principles of Philosophy*

(1644) converted them to mechanistic causation. But recently there has appeared a new understanding of the relation of causes and purposes. *Scientists* have not proved that purpose is absent from nature, but they find purposes confusing and unnecessary as factors in scientific hypotheses. Kepler's account of the geometry of planetary motions was clearer when his explanation of attendant spirits sustaining and directing them was omitted.

The great early innovators in natural science, from Copernicus on, had no desire to shut God out of the universe but only to clear its laws from interference by Him. They believed that His purposes had established the laws and also the law-abiding mechanisms whereby nature works with unfailing reliability and predictability. Mechanism is opposed to this belief. It demands a physical cause for every event, (but no cause for causation!).

Physical science has something new to say about purpose in the world process, however. It no longer takes for granted that banishing purpose from physical equations is equivalent to expelling it from the universe.

Purpose as a mental process implies the use of mind. For strict mechanists, *nature has no mind,* even if she has *produced it.* If human mind and human behavior are part of the machinery of nature, no non-physical, non-spatial purpose can influence any physical event.

When we question life-scientists about causes and purposes, they suggest that we consider the apparent *directional* factor in living processes as distinguished from inorganic processes. They point out that the causal sequences of physics reach no ends. For physics cyclical and reversible processes are as acceptable as one-way processes. Where no end is to be reached, going backwards undoes nothing. Living processes are irreversible because it is their nature to reach ends and to hold to what they have attained. Are then living processes purposive?

Living things, as organisms, have attained an end in *being alive* and in being able to maintain the processes of living. Organisms are self-maintaining, self-preserving, self-perpetuating. This self-maintenance which we call life, with its irreversible processes, seems to link up with the more fundamental form of self-maintenance which we know as the conservation of mass-energy as if it were related to the "whole of things." Science may admit teleological (purposive) conditions as existing on our earth but for the most part refuses to pronounce a verdict on the "whole of things" which with "infinite stretches of time" must always remain outside of any one scientist's experience and therefore be beyond proof.

The world unfolding itself in the great successive steps we have noted in evolution from inorganic to organic, from non-mental to mental, then from sub-rational to rational appears not as the multiple world we might think but as a single, unified world with each new achievement resting firmly upon, supported by, and evolving from the previous one.

Along with these steps, numberless mechanisms have been developed and become established, such as basic food production by means of photosynthesis in plants; the organization and equilibrative control of the elaborate physiological molecular processes which sustain the increasingly complex organisms; the mechanisms whereby the mingling of genes from two parents is secured in both plants and animals, bringing about variations from new combinations; the changing forms of any evolutionary series through the selection of their differences. These may all be claimed as ends which have assignable worth. They are achievements without which human beings as we know them could never come into existence. From the preservation of these ends by the processes of nature, their value in the whole of things is suggested. But could we be justified in claiming such value unless we could prove that the means by which the ends had been reached were selected from many other possible sets of causes? Is there any evidence of the selection of means?

The mechanistic believer in evolution relies on causality alone. This indicates an *unavowed assumption* that "changes of form being implied by the constant motion of the ingredients of the world, *given sufficient time all possible forms must be arrived at, all possible arrangements of the ultimate units of the world,* so that eventually organisms were bound to happen."

Hocking examines this very common and plausible assumption, illustrating it by an imaginary but carefully reasoned experiment, concluding as follows:

> The common belief that in infinite time the stuff of the world must arrange itself in every possible way, therefore in this present way, is one of the few errors of which we may conservatively say that it is infinitely wide of the mark!
>
> We may then assert that the assumption on which the naturalistic emergentist relies is unfounded; *form has no*

> *inherent tendency to rise.* If it does rise, it is as if the series of shapes which constitute the causal history of the universe were selected from an infinite number of possible other shapes, and the grounds required for applying the idea of purpose are present. Emergent evolution is as if it were the result of intention.[35]

Can the evolution of our universe, of our solar system, of our earth and its organisms be regarded as more than a series of chance happenings? Has it a purpose? Is it the expression of purpose? Evolutionary history, as is any history, is a series of events with a meaning. This is an important matter to us, not only because it concerns our very existence, but also because it bears upon any significance our lives may have or any possible meaning they may hold. If all fields of evolution can be explained by their causes, is there still room for explaining them by purposes?

In everyday experience we read purposes (or motives) into human conduct as a well-recognized risk. When we venture beyond organisms into the universe of science or into the "world-view" of philosophy, the risks are greater still. Certainly, before we can impute purposes to the processes of evolution and to human existence, we must have positive grounds for doing so. When have we such evidence?

Science rightfully considers purposes as unobservable and incalculable, and therefore outside its field. But no one denies that scientists have purposes, or that science is a purposive pursuit; it has goals to reach, needs to meet, ends to attain, and uses to serve. The exclusion of purpose from the calculations of science is a purposive exclusion, self-imposed and consistent. Outside that special object, however, the exclusion ceases to be to the point, and the grounds which have led mankind to think of the universe as a result of purpose commend themselves to us. Hocking says:

> The scientist cannot deny the non-physical fact of his own purposes; and since purpose can never be extracted from causes, the existence of purpose in his own being has to be referred to an outer order of its own kind.[36]

A universe with slightly altered proportions of the same materials—a little less nitrogen, a little more oxygen or carbon—would have made impossible the organisms we know or any other organisms unless many laws were changed. To call earth biocentric, as Henderson does, suggests a principle of teleology in the structure of the universe, a possibility of purpose which the criticism of teleology does not meet. If cosmic purpose is indicated in this series of events, their interrelatedness and their capacity to evolve through nature's mechanisms, must such purpose be attributed to mind? Is there evidence of mind of such cosmic proportions and purposes?

Some thinkers are able to think of the universe as an organism. When, as a practical experience, you notice that any report of prominence in the activity of sun spots is accompanied by static on your radio and with disturbances throughout entire broadcasting systems, you are impressed by the interdependence of events in the universe. Others, while recognizing the interdependence, find more relative independence than is compatible with organic unity. It seems nearer the truth to think of the universe as offering an environment for all evolving living things, rather than as itself an organism with no environment. In Hocking's words:

> What interests us is not that everything shall be living and of mental kind, but rather that the universe should offer itself as an arena for life and purpose, an arena whose very wildness, waste, vastness, unspanned gulfs of distance, offer incentives without limit to an ever-growing mentality. Seen in this way there is a purpose in the purposeless aspects of the world; the personal finds use for the impersonal, the living for the mechanical, the intense focuses of consciousness for the infinitely expansive unconsciousness of mass and energy fields. If the world is definable as an environment for purpose, then by this definition it *has* a purpose and is referred to a purposing being for its ultimate account.[37]

The intelligent intentional creativity we experience in a natural product like humanity leads us to believe that a like source of creative purpose may be present in the natural process considered as a whole, a purposive Being who is all that is purposive in the universe beyond human purpose.

It is both possible and plausible that there is in the world something more than nature: namely a purpose to which this nature of ours conforms. Is purpose of cosmic dimensions a reality to you?

Other creatures than man never worry about reality, nor life, nor death, nor destiny. But these are fundamental questions in philosophy, and our decisions about them put us into one of three basic groups:

1. Naturalism takes nature as the whole of reality. Nature is all. It includes man and all his works.
2. Dualism finds two realities, mind and matter, eternally distinct and irreducible.
3. Idealism believes that all reality is of the nature of

mind, and all the world an appearance of mental reality depending on mind for its very existence.

Let us examine these basic types in broad but brief outline to find which seems to reach reality for you. We gain intellectual power slowly, but always by choosing what is simplest and most fundamental in experience as a foundation for building.

To find the realities which appearances may conceal, we need to use the steady observations which science fosters, the logical reasoning which philosophy practices, and the penetrating insights which the intuitions of religions reach.

CHAPTER EIGHT

Naturalism

Naturalism is the type of philosophy embodying the belief that nature is the one reality—the whole of reality. Nature is all. The natural or real world, the whole of human experience is the only world we can know, the only world our senses reveal as existing. Whatever we can know is a part of nature. Naturalists believe we can know no supernature, no "other world," no "after life."

The term naturalism is often used as equivalent to materialism, but the radical changes in physics have so altered our concepts of matter that the word naturalism is now preferred.

Naturalism and idealism are the two main currents that characterize the stream of human thinking. In order to get a true insight into the causes for divergence of these two philosophies, we shall have to ignore much of the complexity and richness of the *whole* from which the two branches arise.

The differences between naturalism and idealism are

deeper than a point of view. These two are as basic as the positive and negative charges of electricity in modern physics. They are the two poles of belief in their appeal to our reason. To one or the other each beginning philosopher is drawn. But we need to try to understand both.

Time has not softened the opposition of thought which was recognized 2500 years ago. It remains because the fundamental issue is not wholly a choice between the implications of these philosophies as embodied in the universe and in our human experience. A material universe is of necessity mechanical, mindless, purposeless and non-moral. Idealists, believing in all reality as mental, view their world as living, minded, purposive, and having a moral structure to conserve the values held by human minds. They feel themselves as part of the same cosmic order as the universe, related to the creative world-spirit with a chance of outgrowing their weaknesses and limitations.

Naturalists believe that from birth to death, nature, however vast or minute, is all we can know—the basis of all our experience. Nature includes the farthest reaches of the stars and the sub-atomic structure of the smallest microbe; it includes man and all his works, his wars as well as his symphonies. It is a nature of law and order, with a continuity among all phenomena—a cosmos and not a chaos, discovered through mind, a region of knowable regularity which we can depend on and which the work of science reveals, pushing the boundaries of knowledge farther and farther back at the expense of ignorance. Nature is productive. It has produced life from the non-living, the sentient from the non-sentient, the reasoning from the non-reasoning. Through this long process which we have come to look upon as an ascent, a struggle toward more complicated forms, it has produced ourselves.

Naturalists do not need to ask what causes nature. It is the sum total of all causes, each one of its phases leading to the next phase. What exists now is competely explained by what has been. Naturalism admits no other cause, no creator, no *first cause,* no *final cause,* no *cause* for *causation.* Thomas Huxley said long ago, "The admission of the occurrence of any event which was not the logical consequence of immediately antecedent events would be an act of self-surrender on the part of science."

Naturalism contends that, as far as experience teaches us, the world-order is a mechanical order, mindless, purposeless and therefore non-moral. In an always indifferent and sometimes most difficult environment, there is only such goodness and value as man himself can make.

Naturalists accept man as one of many animal species. The possession of mind and consciousness do not remove him from this orbit of origin. They regard mind as a tool in the struggle for survival. The intelligence which mind furnishes represents more power, more scope of action for its possessor, but it may be used for evil as well as good. They regard the natural order as continuous, with man representing no break in its continuity.

To naturalists, human nature, despite its mental uniqueness, is no evidence of divine nature. A supernatural element has no basis in the experience of naturalists and therefore should not be accepted as fact. The mystics who claim the experience of divine presence and of divine revelation are considered martyrs of self-deception.

Naturalism relies for its conclusions on such methods of responsible inquiry as are familiar in scientific investigation. Its inferences must arise from fact and from experience and must be checked by proof. It believes that such methods are applicable to the human concerns of religion, art and morals; that things and events, however spiritual, purposeful and rational, are "conditioned in their existence and occurrence by causal factors within one all-encompassing system of nature."

There are in naturalism, as in any type of philosophy, variations in details of belief and in weight of emphasis. In any brief summary we must allow for these. Whatever the variations, the basic ideas remain the same.

Naturalism implies determinism. There can be no freedom of the will in nature. Your acts are determined by the causal processes which flow into you and out from you. Your behavior is part of the machinery of nature and is decided for you, as is that of stars and atoms, and is governed by the same laws that govern them. We probably all have a common-sense belief that we can do as we choose. If that is freedom, we are doubtless free. But as Herbert Spencer reminds us:

> You always do as you please; you cannot do anything else. That is where nature has you; what you please to do is what nature has caused you to please. You can do as you please but you cannot please as you please.

Your apparent choice is the medium whereby nature works her will in you. Nature's determinism is as final as the predestination of Calvinistic theology with a mechanism as rigid as foreordination. If your choices are the results of natural law including heredity, hormones, and habit, you are not morally responsible. Is there, then, any conscience? any duty? any sense of obligation, any concern to decrease the evils of this world and increase good?

Naturalism in its belief about moral responsibility does not leave life without standards of ethics. The motives change; there is no anger of God to fear, no future punishment to face. Death, it claims, is man's end and that of all other creatures. But one's happiness still seems to depend upon the well-being of others as well as one's self; and the way of happiness seems to be that of Spencer's "greatest good to the greatest number." Unrestrained selfishness and sensuality can make a hell of any life here and now. The wrath of society may be harder to bear than the thought of a future wrath of indefinite quality. Naturalists acknowledge the intrinsic value of morality as a basis for a universally accepted rational morality. There is in nature's human mind a recognition, however unformulated and untaught, that self-restraint and decency are in line with one's own growth and satisfaction. For naturalism, evolution is still considered an ascent—a trend toward higher forms—with its chief field at present the character of human beings.

Naturalistic psychology explains religion as a natural and (for a time) useful human mistake. The spiritualistic view of the world, common to most of the great religions, recognizes the existence of divine beings of greater power and worth than human beings who rule an unseen world which is somehow veiled from our senses and yet is in communication with the world of nature and within its easy reach if one knows the path. These powers or agencies, which we distinguish as divine, know and care about us, may intercede for us, guide and protect us. We are not so sure of our relation to them, but we are taught to respond to these powers with a certain homage of obedience and worship. We recognize certain ways of living which are in harmony with these divine powers and certain other ways which are not. These can be known. This world of nature may not last; the other world is eternal. Our bodies die, but our souls at death—the harmonious ones—pass into this other world.

Such beliefs, says naturalistic psychology, offered encouragement to the hard pressed lives of earlier man. The great task for man's mind, if he was to be strikingly different from other animals, was to be able to look ahead to a future, to be interested in it, and to plan for it. He had dreams; perhaps his creative imagination was his most distinctive faculty. He might live these dreams in that other world and round out his hopes, overcome his obstacles, and work out his reward with the supposed help of divine power. Religion held him in devotion to an ideal through the many difficulties that attended all primitive living. It created an emotional background of enthusiasm (an inner god), guiding the feelings into orderly channels which bound a community together in fellowship and in the respect for leadership.

Naturalism expects a man to discard his dreams when he judges them as such. It does not destroy all that man has treasured under the term *religion.* It substitutes, in place of a supernatural being for whom naturalism finds no proof, a more limited being, *Humanity,* whom we have with us always and whom we can loyally serve. The idea of God seems to the mind schooled in naturalism to be a passing form of a permanently necessary devotion to ideal social needs; and the wish for immortality seems to be the longing to finish out the unfulfilled hopes and dreams of this life—another chance for nearing satisfaction and perfection. To understand the psychology of our beliefs is to free ourselves from them. So to naturalists religion, while not disproved as a human need, is considered unscientific, outmoded and outgrown, notwithstanding its former usefulness and our deep intuitions.

Man is the most interesting fact in nature, but not many of us can deify him. We often find his wayward heart disappointing. You may be able to regard him as part of nature's mechanism, but a knowing mechanism is a paradox. What his knowledge is, why he believes it, how he gets it, what it signifies, what it implies, its relation to truth, are problems yet to be solved.

At heart naturalism may have a piety all its own. Its deification of nature has contributed to the modern religious belief that whatever God is, He is near to each of us, around and about and within us—not a distant, divine ruler. This has forwarded the belief that if spirit in which we live and move and have our being is something poured out on earth, the simplest facts must contain it and account for the embodiment of the world spirit in the facts of sense. But naturalists feel they can know nothing about God, and do not need Him. Nature has its own sublime dignity. However indifferent nature is, it deals impartial justice. It is absurd to pray to it, but you may question it endlessly. It hides no secrets, heeds no charms nor incantations, feels no irreverence. The weak may be crushed, the knowing rewarded, but under the working of nature's laws, disbelief is not punished; it may lead to learning. You escape doubt by use of reason and experience.

The negation of other-world realities means that naturalism rejects not only the religious ideas of God, soul, immortality, miracles, but also admits no freedom of the will, no moral responsibility, no providence, no room for guidance nor control other than that bound up in the nature of things themselves. There can be no intervention, no creative influxes; our metaphysical horizon contracts; our problems grow simple. The idea that physical events could be immediately ordered by the hand of God in relation to human interest, naturalism dismisses as a dream. To naturalism the laws of nature are the only omnipotence; their observed uniformities, the only causal agents. Fields of knowledge not yet explained by natural law will eventually be brought within our understanding as have been causal psychology, release of atomic energy, electronics, weathers and (some think) dreams.

Naturalism does not consider conscious reason as an original and permanent fact of the world. Human mentality is transitory, a feature evolved out of lower organisms, and ultimately out of physical things which may be considered wholly inanimate. Why should reason not flicker out into the inanimate whence it came? The enduring realities of our universe do not think nor plan. "Mind, having evolved as a food-seeking device, is not more to be trusted as a truth-finding implement than a snout of a pig." There is no purpose nor reason for the world as a whole.

Naturalists repossess the domain of the human spirit for those philosophies which recognize the natural sources of spirituality. They respect ideals no less because their origins and conditions are in the realm of natural existence, which includes human nature itself. Naturalists see nothing more unnatural about man's purposes, values, and ideals than about the seasons and the stars.

Whatever we may think of these negations held by naturalism, experience inclines each of us strongly toward this type of philosophy. Nature is always asserting her rights to be considered as reality. Our daily interests and pursuits are our realities. Yours are not the same as mine, but I honor yours as being as real as mine, which may be a microscope and all it reveals, or thought expressed in words on a printed page. For all of us there are the activities connected with food and drink, clothes and shelter, work and play. Gandhi may have sustained a fast for many days, but to most of us, a few extra hours without food reveals a humbling dependence of our minds and dispositions upon that common need. We can decrease our hours of sleep, but not omit them. We can increase our hours of work but can not continue them uninterrupted. We can prolong our lives but not escape death. Death ends our communication with personality. Can we find any tangible proof that the human spirit escapes the fate of the body? The mind has developed with the body; both have shown how easily they are affected by changes in food, fatigue, temperatures, altitudes, conditions of health or depression. If the powerful forces of fire, flood and pestilence are kept from bringing injury to human life, it is because some human will has intervened, built dams or levees, erected watch towers, safeguarded water supplies or otherwise used one natural law to control another natural law. There are no other powers to act in our behalf.

The two groups of phenomena which have given the greatest difficulties to explanation by naturalism are life and mind. These stand out from the general principle of nature that like comes from like. The point at which life must have come from inanimate matter has to be described as that time when protoplasm reached a certain stage of complexity. But protoplasm as we know it comes only from pre-existing protoplasm. It has never yet been produced synthetically in a laboratory. It is dead before we can analyze it into its constituents, and when we bring the combined chemicals together *nothing we can yet do* organizes them into living cells. The problems involved may some day be resolved, but as yet they seem insoluble. The point at which the sentient must have arisen from the non-sentient is equally difficult to explain; matter energy does not behave that way; facts are not conscious of facts; man's mind *is*.

The constancy and continuity of the living individual's self amid a changing stream of incoming and outgoing substances, we have described elsewhere. "It is the same individual always without having in it the same stuff." Its life is what Spencer describes as "continuous adjustment of internal relations to external relations." However complicated its make-up, it acts as a whole, and acts as if it were trying to preserve its existence. It shows an astonishing resistance to disintegrating influences which it loses after death. These characteristics and activities of the living organism are observable, but the chief characteristic of mind—feeling—is an invisible quality. We know it in ourselves. We cannot observe it in others but must infer it in them from action or other forms of behavior and expression.

At this point, the theory of evolution brings us aid in rounding out the view of naturalism by its explanation of the origin of life and mind. Darwin's work touched this problem only indirectly. He took life as he found it, assuming that it came always from previous life, not attempting to go back to its origin. He convinced thinkers of the truth of evolution because he broke down the lines between species and believed that this proved the relationship between all forms and the progression of higher forms from simpler ones. How life first appeared on a planet which earlier had been unfit for life as we know it and how mind entered on the scene were problems which a generalized theory of evolution first formulated. Spencer thought the gap between the nonliving and the living could be bridged by biologists working with chemists. In the more than a century since that time, great progress has been made in understanding the physiology of living creatures and the marvelous self-balance of the special processes that sustain them, but no life has been produced by synthesis. Organic products, even peptides and urea are made, but *no living protoplasm*. Living tissues grow and live continuously in nutrient fluids, but no bit of such tissue has been organized artificially; no self-directing, self-maintaining, self-preserving organism has been produced except from a pre-existent organism.

The many changes, since Darwin and Spencer wrote their views of the manner in which evolution takes place, lead us to ask again if mind may not have entered during one of the abrupt steps known as mutations. When the gases oxygen and hydrogen are combined in a certain way in certain proportions, the water which results presents these seemingly new and unpredictable qualities—fluidity, visibility, reaction to temperatures, floating when frozen. It may be that life and mind have resulted from such a combination of proportions of physical elements and "have emerged." The term is descriptive rather than explanatory. This picture of evolution as a series of steps in which the living, the conscious, the reasoning may have come from inanimate nature would perhaps have lessened the puzzles with which Spencer struggled, but it has not solved them. As we learn more, other puzzles arise.

The question of the evolution of mind is to be solved partly by knowing what mind is as we now find it. Can naturalism give such an account of human nature as it is, that it will be easier to understand how it came to be? The scientific account of human nature is psychology. It must be measured by our judgments of mind and its place in the world. It must help us in these judgments. It is said that psychology must be the chief battleground between naturalism and other views of the world.

Psychology has for nearly a century been considered chiefly from the point of view of physiology. That is, mind has been considered a function of the brain, and, with the rest of the body, subject to cause and effect as a part of physical nature. The "reflex arc" made the active mind seem a phenomenon of stimulus and response. Instincts were understood as more complicated sequences of behavior into whose make-up a number of reflex arcs might enter. These instincts, adjusted and changed by experience, constituted our habits and thereby the character of the adult individual. However, you may well ask how this simple scheme accounts for memory, planning, reasoning, creative processes.

If we can learn of the mind through behavior which we can observe and measure, is it not reasonable to assume that the acting organism with its marvelously sensitive nervous mechanism is, for scientific purposes, equivalent to the mind itself? This is the position of behaviorism, the extreme development of naturalistic psychology. The question for us, however, is not whether psychology has thrown a great flood of light upon human nature. The question is simply whether the sort of psychology which investigates the mind solely as an object in nature, subject to laws of cause and effect, can tell the *whole truth* about the mind because of consciousness. Remembering that the mind is something of which each man has a specimen close at hand, do you accept this equation of your mentality with the mechanisms of your behavior? Also can you accept yourself as wholly a creature of cause and effect?

The revolution in physics has certainly made naturalism less plausible and less self-confident. But we do not need to judge the sufficiency of naturalism from the highly technical ground of theoretical physics. We find it lacking in its explanation of qualities. Democritus of the Greek world, an early naturalist, said, "Only in opinion consists sweetness, bitterness, warmth, cold, color; in truth there is nothing but the atoms and empty space." At an electrical exhibit we have *seen sound* and *heard light*. As science replaces our simple observations by its discoveries, we know that color is the result of certain vibration rates on our sense organs. Vibration does not explain color in the sense that color is derived from vibration, but differences in vibration rate may explain differences in color. The physical fact does not produce the mental fact, but changes in the one correspond with changes in the other. The quality of color is there, and, if it is omitted from the idea of nature, can it really be explained? Naturalism replies that quality is the effect of a certain vibratory disturbance upon the sense organs, nerves, and brain of the observer. If the sense organs, nerves, and brain are themselves physical objects, they are composed of the same kinds of materials as other physical objects. If there is no color in the object that causes the vibration, neither is there any color in the eye or brain, and so it is with sounds, smells, textures, and other sensory experiences. Then what *is* their source? Yet they exist for all of us. Naturalism seems to exclude them as a subjective extra which "nature could very well get along without."

If the brain contains no quality, the brain is certainly not the mind. If a motion in the brain accompanies the thinking process, it is evident that the motion must be one thing and the thought quite a different thing. If this is true, brain and mind cannot be considered as equivalent as they sometimes are. Naturalism, however, holds with Hobbes that a sensation is nothing but a form of motion, and a thought nothing but a chain of dying sensations, hence a sequence of motions. When two objects are identical, you can substitute one for the other invariably in all statements. Try to substitute the mental experience, "I am terrified," for the physical experience, "There is in my nervous system and viscera a physico-chemical disturbance of a violent pattern, paralyzing my muscles and erecting my hairs." Descartes showed clear insight when he reiterated, "The essence of the mind is thinking, and thinking is not an event in space." A microscopic inspection of a brain process, were it possible, would, however perfect, simply fail to discover any suggestion of what we mean by thought or feeling. If everywhere else in the world motion produces motion and nothing else, how is it possible that here in the brain motion produces sensation and thought? Does naturalism really explain mind, or does it avoid the issue excluding mind as it excluded sensory experiences?

If you apply the psychology of naturalism to your beliefs, they must be always the effect of some preceding cause. Change the cause and you change the belief. Our philosophy would depend upon the causes that act upon us: the indigestions more than the convictions, since consciousness and its by-products are to naturalism less effective (if at all) than so-called physical causes; the changes in the chemistry of the blood more than conscious reason, since the sensitiveness to such changes is more to be counted on than are the processes of reasoning. If our beliefs are the results of such causes, what is to guarantee their truth, their *reliability* as guides, even in the acceptance of naturalism? But does truth in beliefs vary under different conditions? Do our reasons for these beliefs hold through prosperity and adversity, through sickness and through health?

Naturalism does not account for this constancy in our beliefs, for our minds as knowers of truth. Do you think of your mind as obstinate, as clinging with blind tenacity to beliefs once they are accepted? Have you not been known to change some of your basic beliefs, without change in climate or health or other recognizable external or internal conditions? These changes were probably wholly based on conviction, from new evidence brought by science or philosophy or by discussion with others or through human experience; i.e., through reasons. But naturalism does not count reasons as a link in the chain of cause and effect. If we are so wholly causal beings, why should we feel pride in being considered rational beings, even sometimes at an early age? Why should we feel so frustrated when decisions are taken away from us by bossy persons, when we are managed or imprisoned as "conscientious objectors"? Do such experiences also not suggest that there is something wrong with the assumptions of causal psychology? that human beings are something more than results of cause and effect?

There are many features of our world which naturalism does not try to explain; it considers them beyond explanation to be taken as given facts, not alone by naturalism, but by any philosophy, any view of the world. The constituents of the world, their quantity and proportion and their arrangement, naturalism accepts as given facts. They are here as we find them. We make changes in their arrangement; these we can explain, but naturalism does not try to explain their presence. Leaving these things unexplained may cast doubts on the naturalistic philosophy, but can other philosophies do any better? (Are they able to open doors showing that there is purpose in the universe?) We shall see.

In a way the change brought to our thought by the twentieth century, with its profound revolution in our conception of the ultimate facts of physics, makes no difference to naturalism. It is not committed to any particular physical doctrine but only to an unquestioning acceptance of the physical universe, whatever its ultimate make-up, as an outline of nature. Twentieth century naturalism is more complex, more varied, less typical, less confident. (It frequently appears under the guise of a highly technical type of philosophy called "realism" which we shall not here consider.) Recent writers disclose the feeling of a living quality in nature which indicates that naturalism may be silently turning into something else.

Physical science has been finding that it must use metaphysics in exploring relationships of ultimate ideas. This has shown the apparent clarity of naturalism as an illusory advantage. When we explain the world in terms of physical elements, we are no longer explaining the unknown by the known, but the known by the unfamiliar and unpicturable, perhaps even the unthinkable. Naturalism can no longer find support in the former human tendency to accept the solid as the real.

CHAPTER NINE

Dualism

Before considering Idealism as the second great stream of divergent belief about reality, we may well ask, "Is there no middle course, no compromise view which regards both matter and mind as equally real?" We still hear man described as having body and mind, flesh and spirit, or again, as having a three-fold nature—body, mind and spirit.

Naturalism has presented a strong case to prove that nature is all of reality. Certain purposive and creative activities of human minds lead us to question this verdict of naturalism and to extend our inquiry to other types of philosophy.

Dualism is such a type. It recognizes in the world two contrasting realities: matter and mind, forever distinct and irreducible, the material and the mental. Ever since Plato conceived of the world as divided into material substances (which are defective and transitory) and immaterial ideas (which are real and eternal), there have been dualists. Plato's dualism puts the "ideal over against the material, the universal over against the particular, the perfect over against the imperfect, the absolute over against the relative; and the aspiring spirit must strain toward the immaterial Good against the leashes of the body."

Some of our greatest philosophers have been dualists. Their best efforts to understand things rationally brought them to an acceptance of this pair of contrasting realities, mind and matter. Dualism recurs in the history of thought when some philosopher grasps the uniqueness of mind and its qualities and reaffirms its reality. Descartes early felt that he must separate his thinking self of which he felt so undoubtingly sure as a "res cogitans" from the physical world "res extensa." Kant, with his keen perception of the unique quality of mind, regarded Descartes' "field of extension" as a property or function of the mind itself, but he also believed that there was an "unknowable reality outside the mind at whose incentive the materials of sensation appear to us."

More modern dualists like Sir William Hamilton infer from the fact that the phenomena of experience are of two sorts—physical and mental—that there must be two kinds of substances which underlie these phenomena. Other dualists consider the search for *substances* behind phenomena to be futile, and hold that two kinds of reality are revealed through immediate experience. The fact that the evolution of mind and body has to be considered as if these were independent entities appears to the dualist to strengthen the case for dualism. But this may be based on the limitations of our minds rather than upon the reality of this independence.

McDougall's *Body and Mind* is an extended argument for dualism and against a monism of any sort. He bases his argument against materialistic monism and in favor of the efficiency of mind as a factor in life and thus as a primary reality, upon the unity of consciousness, upon the fact that meanings have no physical analogues, upon memory which he thinks inexplicable on mechanical grounds, upon psychical research, telepathy, and upon animal and human behavior.

Though dualisms through the ages have divided the world in different places in deciding its realities, all have held to the existence and independence of some mental or spiritual reality. Those who group the world's great thinkers into disrupters of thought and into the smoothers and settlers of thought find that the disturbers are often dualists. Plato, Descartes, and Kant were all disturbers of great force. Each stimulated unprecedented consideration of these problems which we find still persisting. Bergson is another disturber whose mind seized upon the uniqueness of life as contrasted with the mechanisms of the energy-systems of a satisfied naturalism. In doing this, he credited life with all the attributes of mind, but he expressed a new understanding of the qualities of life. He believed that men could feel the central pulse of the life of the world in its unity by direct perception, by intuition. This central pulse, *élan vital,* was his reality. His stimulating thought and belief in intuition emancipated many thinkers from the shackles of naturalism. He gave us a new grasp of the creativity of evolution instead of the strongly intrenched doctrine of mechanical evolution. In his *Creative Evolution* Bergson claims that life is in its own nature creative and that evolution may be considered a result of an experimental vital impulse.

The relation of mind and body is the most vital problem

of dualism. After establishing the two realities of mind and body, our chief concern is the relation of these two. How is a union of these dual aspects of man's intricate nature possible if mind and body are independent and distinct entities? Does the partnership begin before birth? Can the mind be sure of finding a brain and nervous system fitted to its future range of expressiveness however extensive that may be? How does this union work? Does the development of the individual recapitulate the evolution of the race in establishing the mind-body partnership? The new individual is a bud, stemming off from a matter-energy system which has without intermission been stemming off buds of its pattern for more than 20 million years. The continuum is seemingly a material one and therefore traceable. But what about the mental components of these individual buds? These, being inaccessible to sense, are difficult to trace as continuous. Does the psyche *lapse* at the beginning of each generation, to be synthesized by responses later, or does it lie dormant as in a seed, awaiting the right conditions for its development, establishing itself after birth as user of the implement of the physical organization already so perfected? Or may it perhaps be a reality from the beginning, but not recognized by us because it is beyond reach of the senses? No one tells us when a demonstrable mental factor first makes its appearance in the organization we call the human being. Sense organs such as the eye and ear develop before birth to a degree of perfection almost unbelievable, considering the fact that they attain this complicated and delicate structure in the complete absence of the light and air in which they must later do their work and without the stimuli to which they are to respond. Is a mind also fitting its growth for this cooperation with the body?

Sherrington in a presidential address before the British Association for the Advancement of Science in 1922 said, "The *how* of mind's connection with its bodily place seems still utterly enigma." It still seemed so to him in 1949.[38] If mind and body are two different realities, what theory have the dualists, who hold this position, formed of their association?

Two theories have been formulated, *parallelism* and *interactionism*. Proponents of each of these would have us think of mind and body as two processes rather than two substances. Each asks what have the processes which form our mental history to do with these other processes which make up the history of the brain? Parallelism states that brain processes and mind processes run along together with perfect synchronization and correspondence, without any interaction. Interactionism states that brain processes and mind processes each affect the other. There seems to be no other alternative; they either do or they do not affect each other. But how? Neither adherent makes any claims of the passing back and forth of energy from brain to mind or mind to brain. The brain behaves just as a physiologist would expect it to. But the mind—has the physiologist expectations to be met? It is a human trait to give up habit and regularity in order to make some new adjustment. Mind and body may form an harmonious union, but if two *independent* realities, mind and body, each go their respective ways, their *perfect working cooperation* seems highly improbable.

But if mind, by its parallelism, really makes no difference

to the body events, why it should exist at all is not explained on Darwinian principles. Or if the mind has the same experiences whether the body is there or not, why is the body not superfluous? Would we have to adopt Spinoza's double aspect theory—mind and body, two aspects mediated by an underlying reality? This is a monistic position. But first let us consider the second hypothesis. The theory of interactionism has the great advantage of seeming to be in agreement with our generally accepted common experience that the body affects the mind and the mind affects the body. This gives back to the mind the sense of usefulness of which parallelism deprived it. From this position the conscious intelligence with which we meet life's emergencies has some worth in the struggle for existence. Our thinking does something which the physiology of the brain could not do. Interactionism gives us back our sense of responsibility, our feeling that our wills are of some avail, that we are not mere onlookers, but can *do* things for reasons of our own—even to changing some of the physical aspects or facts of our world.

We have, however, no scientific way of knowing how mind can interact with body. A rock may crush a plant because they are of the same order of being; but how can a rock crush a wish or be affected by a thought? Force and mass have no power over ideas. Ideas do not exert physical force nor yield to mass. Many scientists, perhaps most of them, deny the possibility of such interaction between mind and body.

The real weakness of interactionism lies in the fact that, while seeming in agreement with our everyday experience, it is radically different from it. Neither the mind nor the body can accept the position it forces upon them. The mind is left with nothing to do except what is not accounted for by physiological processes and their interpretation. Since to dualists this explains almost everything, this leaves the mind with little to account for. When we drive an automobile there is no division of labor, our bodies making the machinery function, our minds guiding through traffic to avoid other cars and reach our destinations. In our experience *we do* all of it. What our bodies do, *we* do. We do all of our voluntary actions, however much the mechanisms of bodily processes or of instincts or of the use of machines may enter into them. In our experience the body is not something else than the mind. It seems an organ of the mind and really a part of the mind itself.

These two attempts to explain the relation of mind and body have very little to say about *how* the relationship works, *how* its effectiveness is brought about. In experience, each self acts as a unit with no sense of tandem or team technique. Whatever we do, we do as a whole person—a body-mind partnership, if you will, but as a unified self. We are supremely unaware of our organs and of the approximately one thousand billion cells whose aggregate makes up our living bodies. Each cell is an individual self-centered organism. Each does its part in this amazingly complex whole as if it were interested in preserving the strange constancy maintained in an ever-changing flow of materials into it and out from it—its metabolism. We know of its system of chemical signals, we know of its nervous system as a means to awareness of and a mechanism of adjustment to surroundings, and also as a means of communication between its parts. But this marvelous wholeness and unity of intricately diverse parts—how are they maintained? If the whole governs the parts and regulates their processes in such a way as to contribute to the efficiency of the whole, how does it exert that control? How is the unity of the whole established and controlled in spite of the partial autonomy of the different parts? Cannon's *Wisdom of the Body* and Henderson's studies of equilibration in the blood make important contributions, but the problem remains unsolved. Life still seems a riddle and the relation of mind and body one of its most puzzling aspects.

It is easy to understand why the great dualists are disrupters of established thought. They have grasped a real distinction in the world and have so emphasized it as to leave a set of unsolved problems in many minds. How can these independent and unlike realities cooperate? and how, if really independent, have they come together with such intimate and intricate fitness?

These questions seem unanswerable by the mind and body dualism. But there is in established thought a sort of world-view, a cosmic dualism, which sees in the universe a large series of contrasting factors working together: light and darkness, heat and cold, summer and winter, wheat and tares, vice and virtue, pain and pleasure, good and evil. In the world, contrast or even conflict of opposites can more fairly represent the whole situation. Yet, here too, we ask dualism to explain the relation between the opposing factors and to tell us if they are independent of each other in reality and substance.

Religion with its strong ethical interest in good and evil, right and wrong, has often tended toward dualism. This type of thinking would relieve the divine principle of having created the evil it is engaged in fighting. But the Divine is not supreme if something else exists of its own right as well as He. So religion demands unity, one reality; hence its dualisms have often been transitory or inconsistent in favor of one supreme independent reality.

In evolution the difference between pleasure and pain has played an important part in warning living creatures of resulting benefit or injury. This pair is doubtless more effective because of its element of contrast. Indeed, members of these pairs bear a strong family resemblance to each other; day and night are both relations of position of the earth to the sun. Heat and cold are both degrees of temperature. They are contrasted only to our sensibilities and to each other, not in their nature. Is this true also of good and evil, of matter and spirit?

Is it possible to think of pure evil? If we could separate all evil from good, would evil vanish? The question arises, would not good vanish also? That is, is not some contrast necessary to give good its quality? If pure evil is meaningless, good and evil cannot be independent realities. The ultimate problem of history seems to be that some good is in evil, and some evil is in good. Good that triumphs over evil may yield to the evil that is inherent in the power whereby good tries to maintain itself.

The decision about the contrasted realities, matter and mind, is less simple. We seem able to think of matter without thinking of mind, as if it existed of itself. Descartes thought it did. He also thought that he could form a clear and distinct idea of "I think" without admitting matter into that thinking and that therefore mind could exist without a physical world. Can you decide this for yourself?

Can you think of matter without thinking of mind? The frame of evolution gives us a picture of a universe in its early stages wholly without life and consciousness; space and energy systems may have existed, but not living creatures. If you can think this, you have a fair argument—if you believe with Descartes that our thought is a good test of reality, that the stuff of nature is an independent reality.

But on the opposite side, most of us experience decided difficulty in thinking of mind without matter. When we think, we think of *something,* usually with sense-imagery in it and therefore out of, or drawn from our experience. Nature is the material of experience on which all thinking is based, the grist for the mill of thought. Then does not mind need matter in order to exist?

Think more carefully, however. Does mind need matter, or does it need *simply the thought of matter?* Could such thought exist without the real existence of such matter as an independent substance? Our deep-seated need for unity in our thinking and experience responds to this possibility. At the hazard of losing dualism and the truths it seemed to make clear (only to raise more complicated problems), let us follow this path which Descartes pointed out and examine the way it leads.

Spinoza's thought makes this contribution: Matter and mind, each in turn, seems to us the one ultimate reality, the other, one of its attributes. If both views are true, there can be but one ultimate reality or substance of which matter and mind, extension and thought, are two complete aspects, two equivalent expressions, as if in two languages. So dualism comes back to monism in Spinoza's thought. He judged this ultimate substance unknowable, as nature or God, one self-caused being, the basis of everything in our experience.

Leibniz opened up the vista already suggested; the *thought* of matter might be sufficient without the existence of any real substance to correspond to it. After all, the thought of nature is exactly what we have. When we say that mind needs matter in order to exist, we admit that mind needs nature as raw material for thinking. Is this perhaps the truth and the whole truth about what nature is? This path then has led us to a monism in which the reality of mind has absorbed the reality of nature into itself. This is the belief of idealism.

Idealism is the natural outcome historically of the type of philosophy to which dualism led the course of human thought. Since dualism has arisen repeatedly as a result of a new vision of mind, that concept could not be realized by thinking of mind as an object in nature. Instead it asserts a monism in which mind takes nature into itself. Let us examine the world-view of idealism to see what grounds it offers for its decision that mind is the one primary reality.

CHAPTER TEN

Idealism

Idealism is the type of philosophy which holds that reality is of the nature of mind. It considers matter-energy and the whole of nature as derived from and dependent upon mind. It explains physical nature by mind because what we know about nature can be known only through mind.

There are two objections to the word idealism being used as the name for this view of the world. The stem word was idea-ism, which has the defect of suggesting fragments of knowledge rather than a mental whole. When the "l" was added for euphony, its suggestion of a special relation to ideals was not regarded as a serious objection. Mentalism or spiritualism, more fitting terms, had earlier been given to other uses.

If we recognize in our thinking that the two great aspects of the world which might claim the position of reality are mind and physical nature and then we find all our knowledge of physical nature dependent upon mind, we must give mind the supreme place in reality. Mind is creative, and creative mind seems something more than nature. Idealists believe it easier to account for the world in which we live if we start with mind. In the beginning was mind. If we are looking for reality, we shall find it *mental* in nature. Whatever is ultimately real in the universe is mind. Whatever appears to be other than this, independent of it, or in opposition to it, will be found to depend on mind for its reality—for its very existence.

To the novice, idealists may therefore appear as men, who in Hegel's words, have resolved to try to walk about on their heads. Can you see why these men chose to view the world in this inverted way? If you think it merely ingenious, you will have difficulty in explaining its profound influence on nineteenth century history. We must try to understand the basic beliefs of idealism if for no other reason than that of its significant contribution to the whole course of modern life.

Royce thought of the movement of idealism as the very soul of our civilization,

> . . . not as a specific theory so much as a tendency, a spirit, a disposition to interpret life and human nature and the world in a certain general way—a tendency, meanwhile, so plastic, so manifold, so lively, as to be capable of appealing to extremely different minds and of expressing itself in numerous mutually hostile teachings.[39]

In this country idealism once held a dominant position because it lent intellectual support to the belief in a spiritual origin of things, a factor which is at the heart of all religions. It enlisted the endorsement of some of our greatest thinkers. It has been widely taught in our universities and sponsored by great teachers. Idealism has stood the test of time, and it appears to support the optimistic attitude of our people toward life and the world.

Its leaders think that idealism satisfies both the head and the heart of mankind as does no other type of philosophy. It is described as having its sources in ancient intuitions. While intuitions cannot be considered a sufficient base for any philosophy, we may not be able to arrive at any true philosophy without them. Idealism, as a matter of history, may be considered as an attempt to bring reason into the spiritual intuitions of mankind.

Idealism is a term to be used just now with some caution since it is always a fashion to regard anything that endures as outworn. This has happened to idealism before, but this time, I am told, much attention is being given to a revival of orthodox theology, in which idealism is identified with subjectivism, the world-in-the-mind view of Berkeley and Leibniz. This wholly neglects the essential meaning of idealism.

We must remember that the chief contribution of idealism to the history of human thinking is that the "real" is living and purposeful, not dead fact. This is in the realm of metaphysics, not "a way of knowing"—an assumption to be tried out.

While naturalism and dualism have maintained opposition to idealism, idealism has never been banished and has been at times almost synonymous with philosophy. As an attempt to formulate the order and intelligibility of the universe and human experience, it has grandeur of range and convincing detail. But of late, science has seemed an able ally of naturalism because of its refusal to accept unknowns and its demands for proofs.

Naturalists are satisfied that experience "supplies us with all our accessible knowledge" while idealists question the wealth and depths of insight that human experience can give us concerning our world. They think it important to consider what human reason is able to do side by side and in union with experience. For experience is not mere sense impression. In a rational being, it is a process not merely of receiving sense impressions but of interpreting them. We can think of sensations coming in through our sense organs as the whole of reality, or we can regard them as a summons to think. The triumphs of science have come from *thinking* as truly as from *finding out;* from reason as well as from discovery and observation of facts.

If, as naturalists think, physical things are causes of our perception, they are not our perceptions themselves; and our perceptions, as their effects, are not these things. But our perceptions are what we have of the world; hence we do not have the world itself in our minds but a subjective mental representation of it. Thus naturalism ends in a quandary, for it assumes (as we all do in our spontaneous thinking) that we have the real world before us in our minds. Naturalists claim that all reality is physical. Idealists believe that the primary reality, the only reality ever given us by direct experience, is consciousness and is therefore mental.

Matter, then (idealists think) is not a primary reality since what we can know of it exists in our minds. Matter-energy is a phenomenon, something *other* than mind which we can know only as we experience ideas of it in our minds. With consciousness as the only sample ever given us through direct experience, how can we have any other concept of reality? If the external world is like our ideas of it, it must be a world of ideas. The only thing which is like an idea, is an idea. Hence we must assume things in themselves to be mental in nature.

Instead of looking to science with its matter-energy, its electrons and protons for ultimate reality, idealism turns to mind which has discovered these features of our universe, to its thoughts, intelligence and reason, to all the spiritual ideas and values of mankind. Idealists think that naturalism, with its dependence on science and sensory proof for reality, leaves out much that idealism finds indispensable to a true concept of the universe. Naturalism believes that it can explain mind by physical nature; but its opponent criticizes this concept of human beings as reaction mechanisms without freedom of will or responsibility for decisions. Idealism argues that it is from a knowing experiencing self or mind that not only all meaning and values come, but also all existence; that any system that does not build upon mind as central in life and evolution gives an inadequate (if not false) concept of reality.

In such a universe, where realities are mental and spiritual rather than physical, idealists find a world mirroring man and his activities, his dreams and hopes. Man assumes that he has a destiny and that the cosmos will help him achieve it. His idealism is rooted in the belief that our minds and the thought-world which they build are related to reality in a revealing and meaningful way. We can know what lies at the heart of the world only by looking within ourselves to those activities which may parallel closely the activity which shapes the universe. Our clearest insight into the nature of this activity must come from the mind and soul and character of human personality, even though it has capacity for error and is of finite dimensions.

Naturalists pronounce such belief to be based on wishful thinking, with no supporting facts in human experience. To them the wholly material world is mindless, purposeless and non-moral. It is unknowing, indifferent and can do nothing to help mankind. Man's values are human, changing, shifting standards although working for the amelioration of life's evils.

Idealists think values are permanent, the very essence and core of the universe whose activities and processes are working toward their realization. Humanity and the universe, *both brought into being* by the *World-Spirit,* are working together to bring about good.

Idealism as a theory is supported by the degree to which it can explain why nature exists. Naturalism says that nature exists; to ask a reason is meaningless. Naturalism has no use for meanings. Nature is here—that is the end of it. But the problem is a real one. The early Greek formulation of it led by Plato, moved toward idealism without arriving. Matter was in opposition to the soul, forever impeding its progress. This view of matter, as the negation of all that is of the nature of thought and spirit, pervaded the Middle Ages and continues indefinitely.

Plato's great pupil, Aristotle, gave matter a more important place. Without matter there would be nothing for spirit to embody; without the body, no human mind, no communication between minds. He thought there could be no personal soul separating itself at death and living by itself, for he regarded the soul as the essence of the body, giving it its form. Further, Aristotle thought of matter as the center of *possibilities,* the future of which must depend on the present of the material element, a necessary passageway in the effort of the world toward pure spirit. "Nature was at best a means, at the worst a hindrance and a misfortune."

Post-Kantian idealists saw that their problem had to deal with all the aspects of nature which made the Greeks (and most of mankind in their unthinking moments) dualists. Descartes had emphasized for them the sharp opposition of mind and matter; matter is precisely what mind is not, extension versus thought. The fact that physical nature is spatial, unfeeling, quantitative, that it opposes, thwarts and resists us, makes it the polar opposite of mind. This very hostility and deadness, idealists seized upon as revealing its primary purpose, the very opposition of which mind has the deepest need.

If the essence of mind is will, it must be expressed in action; action means overcoming obstacles; if there are no obstacles, no action, no will, no mind. In work, man learns his first moral lessons: effort, persistence, looking ahead, courage, are sources of his first moral victories. If you can think of world-mind as having purposed the development of a *free moral* being, you can see that the production of a natural setting, having in it plenty of opposition, hardship, effort and danger would be a suitable means to that end. Kant thought that nature exists as a necessary condition of the moral life of finite minds.

Hegel thought that nature is necessary in order that mind may come to attain self-conscious, self-possession. Man must meet ignorance in order to appreciate knowledge. He must see evil in order to know the rightness of good. Hegel thought of the development of life and mind out of nature as the Odyssey of the Spirit coming into its own. He thought the deepest truth of the world is the incarnation of the universal in the particular—of the world-spirit in the facts of sense.

Such conceptions attract the imagination and may lead the mind to a sense of insight into the mystery of the cosmos and our aspiring human hearts, but some people are repelled by such fancies and pronounce such speculation as based on wishful thinking.

At their root lies a simple consideration which we can state with complete literalness. An empty mind is no mind at all. To be a mind is to be occupied with objects and relations. If mind is to have character and personality there must be a difference between contemplation and action, for action is always concrete. It must be possible to think first, to consider possibilities and then to act. Action means that thought enters the world of sense with endless interconnections. In this way the world of sense is a determining part of what we mean by "will." Nature is essential in order that mind may qualify as will.

Thus nature is not only useful to mind; it is necessary because without it mind could not exist as a concrete and active reality. We cannot have nature and mind as if mind could be self-sufficient. Nature is so essential to the very notion of mind, that if mind cannot be a product of nature, nature must be a function of mind.

Idealism cannot give up the reality of mind and its consciousness for the sake of an abstract science of mechanics. We cannot escape from the difficulties of explaining nature by eliminating all facts which, like consciousness, do not fit into the mechanistic pattern dealt with by physics. Modern concepts of science—space, time, ideas of substance, sensation, quantity and quality which are attributed to the objects of the external world—are in final analysis ways in which the scientist regards them. What I perceive becomes mine, I know it, remember it, reproduce it. In this way the world *becomes* my idea. Experience comes in to us from the outside.

The real question for idealism is the *nature* of *this outside and active reality given* in experience. It cannot go back to naturalism and admit a material substance as the basis of all physical objects in a wholly self-sufficient, independent world of nature. It cannot give up its basic belief that reality is of the nature of mind. Objective idealism asserts that there is something beyond self—as real as myself—but believes this outer reality to be not matter, *but other mind.* The reality which acts upon me in sense experience is some *mind,* not my own. The only thing that can limit or act upon a self is another self. Idealism believes that the world is a self—a living, minded self; and sense experience is its impact on a living mind.

When you ask if a direct experience of world-mind is possible, idealists answer that all our experience of nature is at its foundation an experience of world-mind. In its true and original character, nature is between minds—a social experience. To experience nature is to experience world-mind in its creative activity. Idealists claim that it is not in rare and unusual moments of high emotional exaltation that we can have a vision of world-mind, for that mind is present to us in the permanent stream of plain physical sensation—the facts of sense embodying the world-spirit.

Thus nature reveals the world-mind in its creative activity. To a young child every sensation is a sign of an object which arouses an activity of exploration. Investigation is the usual response, as if there were a sense of obligation to know. In the way we accept sense experience as truth, there is an element of moral obligation. Idealists hold that there could be no such sense of obligation to matter, that only a living mind could be such a source. They think that the only thing that can limit or act upon a self is another self, that the world of reality, which is the world of truth, is a world of a universal self—world-mind.

Objective idealism, in its feeling that nature does not belong to your individual self but that it existed before you and will exist after you, agrees with naturalism in this seeming reality of nature. But idealism's belief that all realities are mental is supported by experience of the genuinely creative power of mind. Although the experience of nature is first given to us as an outside agency, we at once interpret it and reproduce what is given us. We receive, then give; we are at first passive then active.

To idealists it is the extraordinary extent and power of this silent activity which alone justifies their hypothesis that a mind could create nature, that the reality behind and within nature could be mental.

Consider what your mind does when dreaming. During sleep, outside events are largely shut out or greatly reduced.

Yet a vivid dream is as concrete as actual experience. It may exceed reality in realizing your highest hopes or in giving form to your deepest superstitions. You do not direct the progress of your dream experience; you are as passive toward it as in your waking experience, taking whatever comes as true. The conscious self has little power to control the happenings in a dream. Yet the dream must be in all its details of appearance and action the product of your mind—your subjective imagination.

In our waking hours the mind is active in much the same way, though its activity may be dimmed by the stronger vividness of actual happenings. Our minds are constantly contributing to the fabrics of what we perceive. We interpret the cry of a child, a sudden darkness, the smell of burning. In watching a magician's tricks we are inclined to see what we expect to see rather than what really happens. In this experience the very stuff of sensation, instead of being imported into the mind, is the product of the mind.

In all these activities of our minds, the materials used have been gathered from preceding experiences, but the varied activity shows that there is nothing given in experience which we cannot reproduce. We are not the creators of our world, but "we may consider ourselves as apprentices in the process of creativity." Out of our store of perceptions, we are learning to produce a world. The reality of this creative power supports the belief of objective idealism that we "have in our own being something like in kind to the activity which produces nature and presents it to us."

We, whose finite minds can create only after we have learned by experience, can but faintly conceive a supreme mind, a world-mind which can bring forth the qualities of experience from within itself without previous pattern. Our thought and will, which justify the term *mind,* must be shared by the world-mind which can not only think the world but can communicate the world-perception to us. We cannot know how profoundly different from our minds this creative world-mind is, but we think that the reality of nature consists in its being willed, and therefore thought, by a creative mind.

Discussing idealism in *Types of Philosophy,* Hocking says that in most arguments for the existence of God as an intelligent creator, inferred from nature as an effect, the Creator is apart from his created world. The view of objective idealism would be that the world-mind, the philosophical equivalent of God, is within the processes of nature. Creation becomes a continuous process. The world-mind does not establish an independent physical world and leave it to evolve its latent possibilities. There is no creation, if creation means a bringing into being out of nothing, a material, law-abiding world. Idealism has no catastrophic creation but rather a continuous manifestation of Creative-World-Mind within the processes of nature.

Those processes are the very reasonings of that mind; the passage from cause to effect is its "drawing of consequences," its consistency of thought and steadfastness of purpose. The growth of science would be the tracing of the world-thought. The fact that science can think the world and can think successful hypotheses can be understood if we consider that the world is nothing else in its nature than an eternal thought.

We cannot think of the world as a finished result of an external designer. Instead "the very march of nature, the change of the world as well as its being, is the working of a present cosmic purpose within the frame of events. Nature is moving from the past into a future—and even if you cannot discern it, there is meaning and value in what now exists and in its motion and in that toward which it moves."

On the problem of freedom, idealism reverses the decision of naturalism which sees human will as wholly deterministic. Idealism says that if the mind builds and controls the body, the body does not build and control the mind. The capacity for self-building is a quality of mind, a visible expression of freedom. When the human mind is acted upon by conditions which cause anger or fear or worry, its reactions are as natural as any other reflex until the mind realizes the cause of its attitude, frees itself from the causal conditions surrounding it, and thereby becomes more real than the causal forces. This power of self-survey is the factor which distinguishes the ways of a mind from the ways of any strictly mechanical process. Kant was right in saying that the mind knows its superiority to whatever is merely natural in itself—its instincts, desires, habits. "Its task is not to destroy these but to use them. Self-consciousness deposes nature from master to servant of the free self."

But freedom gives no mastery of nature outside of self. We can control nothing directly but the meaning of our own deeds. Freedom applies only to our own choices. There are many things in the tides of external physical and social circumstance—age, illness, disaster—which no one can wholly withstand. Death comes to all.

Is the presence of evil with its positive power in our world a necessary condition for freedom of choice? Is it the price mankind pays for his responsibility for his decisions? Good and evil exist in the cosmos and in the human self, even if the inner mechanism of nature is not a lifeless but a moral lawfulness, even if the destiny of the self is not limited by the exigencies of any single space-time order. If the core of our world is creative, purposive world-mind with plans and intentions, will evil be crowded out? Or is it a problem for human minds?

Harvard's great idealist, Hocking, summed up the basic results of thinking and living the philosophy of idealism in a statement so cogent and simple that I am impelled to give it here.

> The idealist recognizes the countless things beyond the power of our control. He believes that nature, with all its apparent indifference to his purposes and its resistance to all thought and will, ought to be there and has certain assurances about his own place in the doings of the universe. If everything is subordinate to mind, then he infers
>
> 1. *Nothing in the world can be meaningless;* for mind acts always in view of meanings. Then, too,
>
> 2. *Human beings,* as among the things in the world, *must have a meaning;* and perhaps it would not be straining too far the apparent work of the evolutionary process to say human beings have a presumptive importance. It would then further follow that
>
> 3. *Human valuations,* however relative to human limitations, are *not contrary to absolute* valuation. Our way of judging values must be essentially consistent with that of the world-mind; for there could be no more meaningless situation than the production by a cosmic process of

a race of valuers whose judgments were at odds with the true judgment of values. Our interest in knowledge, in beauty, and in rightness cannot be entirely off the target. Or, to put it positively, in these appreciations of ours, we must come close to an immediate grasp of the ultimate sense of existence. And if this is true, we may perhaps assume, further, that

4. *Nothing is foreclosed as impossible,* in the direction of our profoundest will; though we have no inkling as to the manner in which such desire is to be realized.

As to death and survival: death, we have said, conquers idealist and non-idealist alike. Only, to the idealist, it is not a lifeless Nature that conquers: it is the law of the world-order, which is a significant order. If it is significant that his own life should survive, the death of the body need not carry with it the disappearance of his finite personality nor of his consciousness. Death, in this view of things, is the destruction of the body, that is—as we were saying—of the *bridge of connection* with this particular group of fellow minds. Death proves nothing as to whether there are other groups of minds in the universe, and other links of connection to be established with them. Whether one survives may well depend on whether one is fit to survive. The less real can in no case destroy the more real.[40]

CHAPTER ELEVEN

The Meaning of Human Life

Meaning is not something fixed and static. Even the meaning of *meaning* may evolve. Meanings may change with circumstances. In experience they become more evident and significant as we grow older, as our discernment matures and our insight develops.

In our present-day life, there is a widespread malady of *meaninglesssness.* No one afflicted by it can say with full conviction that life *has* no meaning, but only that he has not found it. His search, like that during a treasure hunt, may have taken a wrong direction.

We are a young and optimistic people. We have had few punctures in our complacency. There is little of the "canker of disillusionment" which infects the failing cultures where poverty, ruin and confusion have accompanied war-weariness and despair. Yet some people retain a working faith in the meaning of life notwithstanding its tragedies and disappointments. Under the buoyancy of our youth, resulting largely from the very simple and immature meaning given to life, there is often a sense of complete meaninglessness.

Is it true that human life formerly was thought of as an enterprise of more interest and importance than now? With all the expansion of science and its applications, are human horizons contracting? Are factual boundaries crowding out human aspiration and the vistas of a relation to the powers of the universe?

C. G. Jung says: "I should like to call attention to the following facts. During the past thirty years, people from all the civilized countries of the earth have consulted me. I have treated many hundreds of patients, the larger number being Protestants, a smaller number Jews, and not more than five or six believing Catholics. Among all my patients in the second half of life—that is to say, over thirty-five—there has not been one whose problem in the last resort was not that of finding a religious outlook on life. It is safe to say that every one of them fell ill because he had lost that which the living religions of every age have given to their followers, and none of them has been really healed who did not regain his religious outlook. This of course has nothing whatever to do with a particular creed or membership of a church." [41] The restoration they need is a restoration of meaning. For only the meaningful can set us free.

The situation of finding life meaningless is too complex to be clearly analyzed. Sensitive minds of the present-day may be dismayed by the account of the universe that science seems to present. Neither the bewildering complexity nor the inconceivable vastness are the most staggering factors in appalling the imagination; but the modern doctrine of un-knowingness, the indifference, the eternal going on without knowing why, nor whither, are paralyzing facts. Purpose is such a nucleus of human activity, such a directive feature of man's life, that it is hard to conceive it as wholly lacking in the rest of nature.

Let us now bring together some of the fruits of our search. Our first aim should be to consider what meaning may be given to the phenomena of life, and especially of human life, by an adequate philosophy. In the widest sense science does not, as a rule, seek for the meanings of things. It is occupied in the first place with description, and then with explanation. The first task of the scientist, after he has chosen his problem, is to gather the facts which bear upon it. Then, to generalize from these observations, establishing factual laws if it is possible to do so—a process evidently fraught with some peril.

But there remain two other tasks even more hazardous: those of explanation and interpretation. Explanation seeks the most general laws from which the phenomena in question may be understood. Interpretation seeks not laws but meanings. We explain an object when we state what caused it; we interpret only when we can give its purpose, its intention, its significance. We explain a stone wall if we tell how it was built; we interpret if we tell why it was built, what end it serves, how it fitted into the total living of the men who made and used it.

In these two fields of explanation and interpretation, most of the controversies among scientists have arisen; but where questions of interpretation are involved, the cleavage commonly runs deeper than purely scientific issues: divergence of metaphysical assumptions is likely to underlie the differences in scientific opinion. We shall begin with the deepest issue in regard to the explanation of life—is it wholly mechanistic or is the incalculable reality of mind as a directive behind it and in it? Either position is based on an assumption.

In considering the two great but divergent streams of human thought set forth in the philosophies of naturalism and idealism, we have noted their difference of opinion in the matter of a *directive factor* in life and in nature. Since naturalists think we can know nothing about directive factors, they exclude their presence as unknowable and unnecessary. Idealists believe that purpose is a directive factor in human minds and find room for it in the *"whole of things"* —the universe.

To avoid confusion let us distinguish between mind in human beings and the purposive principle which idealists recognize as pervading the universe and which they call *world-mind.* Like the symbols a scientist uses for his equations to show relationships, the term world-mind indicates the mental factors in matter-energy, in law and organization, in life and reproduction, in consciousness and reaction, in evolution and free will, in mentality and ideas—in all reality.

We seem now to understand processes better than purposes. But since human mind is still evolving and is the only factor we know in the universe that tries to understand the whole, we can conceive that human mind developed far beyond its present capacity can eventually come to understand world-mind and its purposes. Human living with its possibilities and its perverseness, its heavens and its hells, may be the only path leading to such understanding.

We have considered the evidence for the presence of purpose in the phenomena of human life. We came to think that there was at least a place for such purpose, and our subsequent study of basic types of philosophy may have helped us to decide this. The difference was formerly designated as mechanism and vitalism. Vitalists claimed that life indicated a new force at work in a previously lifeless world, but we cannot go into that controversy here. The rapid progress of biochemical synthesis increases the belief of scientists that life will some day be produced by synthesis as vitamins and peptides are now. Idealists can accept the capacity for life as part of the constitution of the matter-energy of our universe as they can also think of mind and consciousness as its source and center.

For most of us, life is not as yet explained, though increasingly the activities of living organisms are shown to agree with the general laws of the chemistry and physics of all matter. Even if life's activities are explained by science, their interpretation is still to be sought. What is the significance of the presence of mind and consciousness as it has developed in human beings?

In a way, each of us *interprets* life in our attitude toward it every day. A working belief about life and its meaning distinguishes the human being from the rest of the living world. Since the problems of explaining life and interpreting it differ fundamentally, let us see how naturalists and idealists vary in their power to deal with these basic differences.

To a naturalist, the resources of physics and chemistry can explain all the activities of living organisms; they need no interpretation. To an idealist, mind makes a difference and is to him not simply a mechanism of nature to be explained wholly by chemicophysical laws. An element of intention, a factor of purpose, seems to be indicated. Naturalism to idealists appears to be over simplified, to ignore too many facts to be true.

Most scientists are hesitant before the problem of interpretation since the scientific method is not appreciative but descriptive and experimental. Science has advanced and will continue to advance by the use of mechanistic methods. At the end of the last edition of his great work on *The Cell* (1924), E. B. Wilson wrote, "The inescapable fact remains that the specific reactions of the developing egg depend upon its organization. Concerning the fundamental nature of this organization, we are still ignorant, but we have nothing to gain by the vitalistic assumption that the guiding principle in development is not only unknown but unknowable. Existing mechanistic interpretations of vital phenomena evidently are inadequate; but it is equally clear that they are a necessary fiction." [42] McDougall, commenting on this paragraph in his *Riddle of Life,* wrote, "Here Wilson reveals the belief so common among men of science that visibility together with, I suppose, tangibility on the macroscopic scale, is the essential mark of the real; and holds the belief with the unquestioning conviction which dispenses with any formulation of it in words."

Science can prove that life, both human and other, is an affair of certain self-fermenting proteins (enzymes) catalyzing their own growth. Idealism accepts all the biologist's facts but maintains that life is much more than these facts, that life has *meaning* and is therefore open to interpretation.

Because meanings are unobservable, as is mind, the problem of meaning cannot be solved without making some assumptions.

An interpreter is one who reveals meanings, but a revealer is needed because meanings are not phenomena for experiment or measurement. Because of this, it may be doubted whether naturalism can offer any interpretation of life at all. Does not naturalism logically exclude all meanings? If life can be reduced to electrical charges, are not all events electrical charges, mechanistic opinions included?

Scientific hypotheses are tools for explanation, not for interpretation. In support of the contention that ultimately all biological processes will be reduced to mechanistic terms, naturalists assert that mechanism alone gives a unified and comprehensible conception of the physical world; that the whole cannot be more than the sum of the parts, and therefore may be reduced to terms of the parts (electrical charges, atoms and electrons); that the living body manifests no element nor form of energy peculiar to the living; that non-mechanistic terms such as *vital force* have been dropped from the vocabulary of biologists as unnecessary; that the physical world appears to be governed largely, if not entirely, by mechanical forces; that scientific progress has taken place along mechanistic lines by the use of such methods; that matter and motion are our surest realities; and that consciousness can make no possible difference in the course of events in a physicochemical universe, and may therefore be ignored in the attempt to interpret these events. The naturalist concludes that one, and only one, interpretation of life is valid and that is mechanistic. We live, they think, in a deterministic universe, and the determinism is exclusively chemicophysical. Even the idealist is compelled to admit the force of some of these claims. But there are some which he is unable to grant, and which in his opinion vitiate the entire argument.

The idealist points out that the demonstration that the field of natural science may be mechanistically described is no proof that the entire universe is a great machine. Only on the basis of a naturalistic philosophy could this be true. On the basis of objective idealism and other philosophies, other interpretations are necessary. The philosophy of a mechanist is generally—explicitly or implicitly—naturalism. His mechanistic views derive logically from this.

Science has been able to extend the reach of our senses in many ways—microscopes, telescopes, spectroscopes, oscilloscopes, amplifiers, and many other electronic devices.

In a demonstration by K. D. Roeder of the action of DDT on the nerves of a cockroach, we have seen and heard by oscilloscopic amplification the changes of voltage taking place in nerve impulses and noted the difference between the slight effect of DDT upon the central nervous system and its powerful effect upon the sensory nerves, carrying impulses from the sense organs. When Adrian wishes to study the humanly imperceptible nerve impulses which pass over a fish's hearing apparatus, he can amplify them until they sound like rattling gunfire.

By combining new techniques of detection and amplification, scientists have brought within range of our senses the dimensions of newly available phenomena. We can now "see" and "hear" the effects of the passage of a single electron, the disintegration of an atomic nucleus, the absorption of a proton by an atom.

Every fact that helps to reduce man with his conditioned reflexes wholly to a reaction mechanism; every assumption that robs him of his sense of freedom and responsibility; every study that proves him merely the *product* of his genes and not the builder of a self that uses his gene heritage *creatively;* every disbelief in purpose as a cosmic demand, assails the meaning of life. We may not deny the facts. Within the self-imposed limits of science they may all be true! It is the lack of interpretation, the acceptance of facts as finalities, their negation of experience, that is contracting human horizons rather than expanding them as all truths should do.

Modern man has a great respect for facts. He is just beginning to discover and to respect the *fact* that the better ordering of his life requires the consistent interpretation of facts, the integrative methods of philosophy and religion to supplement the analytical methods of science. Facts mean more if taken as a summons to think than if taken as a finality.

The infinite universe is a structure of truth to which our sensations are only one channel of access. Our thinking and feeling, sympathy and will, reason and imagination may yield equally direct, important and trustworthy responses. Are they any less real than sensations because they are as yet less measurable by science?

Both Kant and Schopenhaur maintain that human minds cannot refrain from asking questions about what lies behind experience. The recurrence of such questions indicates a certain pertinence which deserves an intelligible answer.

If you set about to prove that these mental products may also be results of chemistry and physics, science denies its ability to deal with feelings, thoughts, and other realities that have no existence in space—no measurable qualities. Science and naturalism are partners, both intent on explanations, both inclined to neglect interpretation.

The idealist calls attention to the fact, which in his opinion cannot be reconciled with mechanism, that the most striking consequence of evolution has been the increasing dominance of mind in our world. To him it is the most important, vital, challenging single fact in the universe. He regards mind as the reality whose unfolding *is evolution.* To him the indestructibility of mind may seem far more real than the indestructibility of matter. He thinks mind is the reality with which evolution started, and mind is the reality which science traces in its expanding knowledge of natural laws. Whether the scientist recognizes them as such or not, laws and their uniformities, to most idealists, are an expression of intelligence. Since only mind is intelligent, natural law signifies a living, knowing, purposive universe. Call it world-mind, world-spirit, God, or what you will—the reality must be cosmic and conscious and evolving.

Hugh Stott Taylor thinks that science has drawn far away from the mechanistic, deterministic attitudes that characterized nineteenth century science, but there is still the usual lag in general acceptance of the change. The idealist sees that the mechanical view of things as a whole lends character to its parts and tends to give its quality to the life that is encompassed by it.

The idealist cannot accept the idea of a mechanical universe with its determinism exclusively chemico-physical, great as the laws of these sciences are, because it reduces *human beings,* the highest expression of consciousness yet evolved, to the level of automata, whose intelligence counts for nothing, whose existence is therefore devoid of *sense.* The idealist's world, he thinks, has sense! Mind is its surest reality and evolution its surest intent.

Through the long history of life, evolution has proceeded through individuals. Whether the variations have come through mutations or combinations, whether the new qualities became established or sacrificed, the process has been carried on through the individual. Our democracy is not based alone on the claims of the biological human being, nor on the psychological, but on the whole nature of man. Its aims must satisfy the human heart as well as man's understanding and biological well-being. Its goals must be based not alone on *what is* but also on *what ought to be.* Devotion to a common bond is better aroused if it includes something larger than existing facts, some aspect of the looked-for betterness of aspiration.

The somewhat mythical phrase in our Constitution about all men being created *free* and *equal* was used to justify our attitude toward England, not to change the relation between our slaves and their owners. It may nonetheless help put more heart into those working toward the realization of the truth in the myth, "brotherhood of man." The democracy we fight to defend is based not only on the value of each person, but on the basis of that worth, *individual responsibility.* This is the veritable nucleus of each human life.

In the strictly deterministic world there is no responsibility, no freedom. We are puppets with physics and chemistry pulling the strings, but with no recognition of laws of mind and evolution which involve purpose, thus removing life from the void of meaninglessness and permeating it with meaning. In this the mechanism of the naturalist and the mentalism of the idealist stand opposed.

Dixon in his Gifford Lectures, *The Human Situation,* writes:

> So with nature. Remarkable indeed had been her works had she possessed mind, purpose and foresight, but how much more remarkable, how admirably skillful to produce these interesting things without a particle either of intention or sense! Perhaps intelligence, perhaps brains are a mistake. How much better we might have got on without them! [43]

The idealist cannot forget the double nature of the process of evolution. That it has produced life and the human body is a wonder. That it has produced mind and the *thinker* is more wonderful still.

But is thinking a firm reality to be depended on to prove our point? Naturalism's attitude toward thinking is perhaps best expressed (in lighter vein) in Edman's *Four Ways of Philosophy,* "Thinking is the very late achievement of an uneasy animal in a precarious and changing environment;" to interpret the universe by thought is "as if the tail should think it had invented the procession of which it is the tail." [44]

Does an examination of the relation of the *human bio-*

logical self to the *assumed metaphysical self of the universe* lead to any findings which may combat meaninglessness? This is an important point.

Each human individual is a psychophysical whole, a body-mind, or a mind-body, a self. As a living organism a person is no permanent structure. He is, rather, an identifiable process, undergoing a never-ceasing interchange with an ever-varying environment. Nor is this biological self a possessor of conscious intention or purpose. These are qualities of mind only. The consciousness of the biological self is not directly concerned with details of life processes. It eats because it is hungry, not primarily in order to build its body, nor breathes to sustain it, nor loves that offspring may continue the race. Consciousness is released in sleep and also at times may be completely absorbed with other matters. It is therefore recognized as an advantage that most details of the bodily processes, of nutrition, respiration, circulation, equilibration of chemical content, endocrine secretions, coordination, and reproduction are carried on by what great physiologists have called "The Wisdom of the Body"—with little attention from consciousness. Mind supervises the intake of food where it makes connection with the beginning of the alimentary canal, but is wholly useless in all details of digestion and nutrition. Consciousness can interfere with normal breathing within limits, as when swimming under water, or in talking or singing, but has nothing to do ordinarily with the lifelong rhythms of inspiration and expiration and the interchange of gases between air and body-fluids which they bring about. Mind may not control this or that single muscle but manages groups of muscles in a large and varied number of wonderfully coordinated movements, as in piano playing or interpretive dancing. We recognize the presence of pleasure centers placed at critical control points which insure that all the ends of nature will be met. Biology can only assert that the individual is *built* through the processes of nature, that its form is *preserved* in spite of continuous but relatively slow change and that it is *reproduced.* Biology usually thinks of unobservable mind as a product of the body, but can see idealism's reason for not accepting death as a proof of this relation. Science, as such, can assign no purpose to the individual as a self nor look for any meaning in its existence. If this seems an inadequate interpretation of a human life by science, can idealistic philosophy give a more satisfactory one based on its belief that mind is a product of a minded universe? Can the biologist and the idealist join hands in their effort to understand the human individual? Idealists eagerly accept all the facts of science but not as final truths. Facts need interpretation to reveal their meaning.

When biologists grant that mind is of use to the survival of the organism and that this is biologically its function, they have one clearly defined interpretation or meaning of human life. On the physical level, supposedly, the organism and its lastingness have no meaning—but with consciousness established, everything it cares for has meaning. If it cares for the continuance of the life of the body, as a human being does, then its life takes on the meaning which apparently it had for nature—human life becomes a means to nature's possible ends.

It is surprising that consciousness knows nothing about these ends of nature. As we have seen, mind is not consciously preoccupied with building, maintenance or repair of bodily processes. These are taken care of as factors in the body's own drives—leaving mind in a position which changes the course of our search. Mind, as we have seen, has ends of its own. Mind can serve only at the cost of *being master.* In other words, since mind is by nature an end-seeking, purposive entity, it cannot possibly seek any ends not its own. (The whole nervous mechanism is arranged with this peculiarity in view, as, indeed, it had to be!) And it is impossible for it (mind) *not* to seek its own ends, whether or not these coincide with the ends attributed to nature.

Having evolved as an instrument and a servant, mind takes its place as master of the house, serving its own ends by directing energy. Certainly men's minds have made nature their servant. They have harnessed electricity, radio waves, air transport, radium emanations, atomic bombs; have built vast dams to reclaim deserts; have pumped and mined hidden treasure from beneath earth's crust, using her own vast forces to reshape her own immensities until nature may become man's handiwork as he has seemed to be hers. Mind has revealed the truths of science and helped adjust human beings to a life in harmony with its laws.

This reversal of dominance is what is meant by the phrase that means have become ends—the means to nature's assumed interests have become, for the human being, ends in themselves. Instead of eating to live and seeing to live, one may live to see and to eat; instead of being curious in order to know and knowing in order to survive, man wishes to survive in order to find out and to know. "Knowing" is one of man's durable satisfactions; he makes no apologies for this absorbing and often non-utilitarian concern.

A chief difference between human minds and other minds in the organic series, and then between primitive minds and the more evolved human minds, is in the elements of self-questioning and world-questioning, between the self-knowledge and world-knowledge which lie behind the world-model that man builds in his mind. Whether the world can be considered self-conscious or not, it has produced self-consciousness and the capacity for world-consciousness in man and in none other of its products. This sets man apart in any order of meanings. A reflective mind naturally asks: Is there any relation of kinship between myself and you, the living universe that has produced me? I value things; do you? Are you, who made my being possible, like me, a center of appreciation, a self with values, with qualities, with a capacity for the discernment of meaning? Are my sense data a contact between you, a living world, and me, a living mind? Does my sense of meaning and significance have any relation to cosmic meaning? If so, my meanings may not be subjective, products of my human mind alone, but may be objective with a cosmic reality, having a possibility of permanence through all changes of time and circumstances. Meaning would thus descend from the whole to me, a part. The value of experience seems to shift in its significance with varying conceptions of the nature of the whole, the character of the cosmos.

Idealists believe that life has meaning not only because it holds meanings and these parts give significance to the whole but also because meaning descends from the whole to the parts. The individual human life takes on significance from its relation to the larger totality in whose meaning it participates. This *whole* to the idealist is a *living, conscious, evolving world,* a universe which is a self that has never been without *mentality* and *meaning.*

Bit by bit man builds a model of his world from materials brought to him through sense experience, through reason, imagination, sympathy and through thought. He puts life and mind and destiny into the frame of evolution and sees himself in relation to the whole. His model has his present range of expressiveness, his hope of future boundaries of ampler dimensions. It is a model of the world within his mind with himself in it as well as builder of it.

Again a thoughtful mind must question, "What is the relation of me, a valuer, and my values to the cosmic valuer and cosmic values? Self-awareness brings inevitably a capacity for self-scrutiny and self-estimation. Have I, a human unit, any contribution to make to the whole? Can my life mean a permanent deposit toward the dimensions of the whole? Can human meanings retain validity unless they find a place in an objective mind not identical with nature?"

Brinton in his *Ideas and Men* voices the belief

> . . . that man's sense of values is a groping awareness of the organization of the universe, an organization not evident to unreflective men, not provable by scientific methods, never wholly plain to the best and wisest of men, but an *organization,* not a chaos. Over the ages, the clearest common indication of this feeling is the term *natural law,* which to be sure did not mean exactly the same thing to a Stoic, a Scholastic, or an eighteenth-century philosopher, but did to all three mean a faith in the substance of things

> hoped for. Or to put it another way, the very concept of *natural law* means that those who hold it believe that the gap between the real and the ideal, between what we have and what we want, is no abyss, not actually a gap, *but a relation.* Paul summed it up in his *Epistle to the Hebrews:* For here we have no continuing city, but we seek one to come.[45]

As man is more than a scientific fact, so his life is more. He takes the scientific conscience into his life as a partner of his philosophy and religion but not as a dictator. Human evolution seems to step out of the framework of physical fact into the frame of metaphysical truth of larger and more lasting significance—suggesting again the ancient intuition that in the nature of things life is deeper than matter and mind deeper than life.

The measure and meaning of human life bears a direct relation to the measure and meaning of the universe. This justifies our acceptance of the teaching "he that loseth his life shall find it."

CHAPTER TWELVE

Can Man Direct Evolution?

Does evolution mean mere alteration, perpetual change in any direction, or is the ascending level of organization progressing somewhere? Upon this point science makes no pronouncement. It has nothing to say of better or worse, higher or lower. There is still much that science cannot know, much that lies beyond its method. These matters belong in the field of human values. Have such values objective truth or do they shift with changing standards, or evolve to suit conditions?

If all living things with their variety, intricacy and beauty have evolved from the first stirrings of life in primal slimes, can the evolutionary process be considered perpetual? If human mind, which can contemplate, discover, and formulate the amazing pageant of evolutionary history has developed either from or through early self awareness, can we reasonably assume that evolution may keep on working? We have been considering man in the light of evolution, but we must remember that we can consider evolution only in the light of man. He, alone, of all life's products is able to survey its performance and pass judgment on its accomplishment. Man alone can find the evolutionary process intelligible. He is its most significant achievement: he can ponder and determine the implications of this fact. The common belief in the doctrine of progress had built itself deep in human thought. It was accepted as being as clear and basic as gravity. The wars and revolutions during the later part of the eighteenth century did little to disturb the firmness of this belief; but they showed that progress could be interrupted in its advance and that its course was not always smooth and easy.

The nineteenth century showed great advances in science which were accompanied by inventions and enterprises for putting them to use. Witchcraft died out, cruel sports decreased, some slaveries were brought to an end.

Better schools, bigger cities, faster travel, more varied foods, and even education for women came to pass in the first quarter of that century. The term biology was first used in 1802. When about the middle of the century Comte made his list of sciences, they were mathematics and astronomy, physics and chemistry, biology and psychology. He ended the list with the then-unheard-of sociology. The science of man was to be the crown and climax.

Geology was making great advances. There were rumors that the earth had not always been as it now is. Ideas of evolution were cropping out in various centers while Darwin was working on his report of the five-year Beagle Expedition with its strange descriptions of geological formations containing fossils of animals resembling but unlike the present-day forms. In 1859 Darwin published *The Origin of Species.* The disturbing ferment in the idea of evolution appeared to reinforce the popular belief of progress as inevitable and right. The theory of Natural Selection as the means by which evolution had been brought about helped men to believe it, though in its original form it has not stood the test of time.

Evolution as a process of creation implied that the forces which had shaped the universe are still at work, continuous and unceasing. To many scientists it brought a great epoch in the history of understanding the universe. To some it seemed to be as truly God's way of working as the more capricious method of special creation.

When through radioactivity the next great epoch came, abolishing the dogma of the immutability of the atom, men's minds were much more easily adjusted. This new belief did not involve *human origins* nor faith in *verbal inerrancy* of the Bible, but it helped immeasurably in understanding the structure of the universe. Electrons could still not be seen, but Millikan's *Oil-drop Venture* (1909-12) showed that they were neither uncertainties nor hypotheses. Atoms could lose or take on electrons.

But sociology, the science of man, made less progress. Man as a factor in experiments or in social relations seemed too complex to be predictable. He could be perverse. His "heart" could be *wayward.* Man, however, was proving that he could have a part in directing the evolution of the plants and animals he raised for his use. Stocks and strains were being improved by careful selection.

The laws under which evolution has operated are not capricious. Each radical step such as the appearance of lungs and the shelled egg has been explorative, experimental, built upon variations of already existing structures and functions. When such changes led to new environmental realms, new laws were operative. Outbursts of changes appeared: mutations, new adaptation, new variations resulted. Old mechanisms working under new conditions were perfected for new uses as in the establishment of the control of body temperature and the internal nourishment of mammalian young. These changes established new levels of organization. Are these changes of levels controllable and can their trends be directed by human intelligence?

Scientists are sure that if all food plants were "wiped out," they would be able within a few years to produce from wild species, not now in use, as many edible varieties as we now have. These would not be identical with our present kinds, but equal in food worth and taste appeal.

The scientific experimental stations where such work is concentrated "take orders" for improvements as need for them develops. The yearly butterfat yield of milk from cows has been doubled by careful selection of their sires. A breed of sheep is established whereby twin births are the rule, not the exception. Persian lamb may now be produced in this country from a hardy stock developed by crossing the Persian with a sturdy native strain. Pigs "rolling in fat" are bred when heavy demands for lard exist, while a more "streamlined" variety is advised when the lard market declines. There is still hope that "bees with longer tongues and better dispositions" may be produced. Wheat resistant to rust, pasture grasses suited to Florida's soil and climate, beets richer in sugar, and a host of other successes have been firmly established. Man has proved that he can direct evolution in plants and animals toward desired ends.

Man's genetic approach to *human* evolution, however, still lags in its adaptation to facts. Can human evolution be directed in the human group and in the individual?

In the human race two methods of race improvement have long been recognized. The first, *eugenics,* aims to increase the better-than-average stocks of human beings and to decrease the poorer ones. The term was coined in Darwin's time by his cousin Francis Galton, an early and distinguished student of heredity. Eugenics is based on the knowledge that biological progress depends upon changes in the germ cells. In 1554 Jean Fernal wrote in *Medicina Paris:*

> The beginnings of our being are therefore of much matter to us: those who are of health by birth are not a little fortunate. By consequence it would be a great good for our race if solely those who are sane and sound gave themselves to the making of children. For if the husbandman know that for the sowing of the land the best seed is to be chosen, having found by experience that from a poor seed we can expect only a miserable harvest, how much more strictly should that be practiced in the propagation of our species.

The second method is termed *euthenics,* which aims to improve environment. If evolution is partly a process of adaptation to environment, obviously much depends upon the character of the surroundings. The qualities of each human being result from the interaction of intrinsic, germinal factors and of extrinsic, environmental ones. While both are inevitable in the development of every individual, the eugenist emphasizes *nature* while the euthenist stresses *nurture.* The two are unavoidably complementary. Both aims are now included in the field known as *eugenics.* After decades of activity, eugenics is now ably implemented with evidence from many lines of investigation, controlled experiments, carefully kept records, and scientifically compiled statistics. These give new power and importance to its maturer vision of needs and possibilities.

Naturally, environmental factors have proved much more manageable and measurable than germinal ones. As a result, eugenics has given less attention to pure genetics and devoted itself more to interpreting the "increasingly discriminating" research of the effect of environment on growth and development. The new trends based on new statistics still need to be combined with the fundamentals of genetics to keep a perspective acceptable to both science and sociology.

In both these fields *eugenics* is fundamental to the achievement of our ultimate hopes for a better world. We may well ask what will be its place in a world which more than ever in the past requires character and intelligence for the solution of its problems.

Intelligence is a quality of great value to the social group. Some individuals meet their difficulties in life intelligently; others meet them stupidly, depending on how much meaning the facts involved have for their minds. A few persons in any group are quick to grasp what is significant in a complicated situation and to understand the relations of the various factors in a difficult problem. Others show themselves markedly deficient in ability to cope with relatively simple problems or to manage their affairs with ordinary foresight and success, to sift the important from the unimportant. Between these two groups of deviates are all the intermediates included in the term "average man," the general bulk of any population which includes a wide range of variation in intelligence. Psychologists find equal levels of intelligence in all socio-economic groups. They agree that differences in environment cannot account for variations in intelligence between the deviates in the upper and lower extremes, although changes in environment might move deviates above or below certain levels.

Two main problems in our country center in what we know about genetic factors in eugenics: first, the *inheritance* of *defects, mental* and *physical;* second, racial problems growing out of differential birth rates among races whose distinctive physical characteristics make assimilation difficult. A brief survey of these questions has a direct bearing on the subject of this chapter.

Concerning the inheritance of *mental* and *physical* defects, it is natural that public attention and special social and educational services have been more concerned with the handicapped deviates in our population than with the gifted. The unfortunate persons whose capacities and achievements fall below the standard of normal abilities are often unable to care for themselves. Some cases of feeble-mindedness are caused by illness, accident, or injury to the central nervous system, but most of them are due to some factor in inheritance. Whatever the cause or causes, the problem for us is a double one: How to *care* for them? What can be done to *decrease the number born?*

Various estimates of the reduction of feeble-mindedness, which would result from total prevention of births among definite cases, range from one-tenth to one-third in a generation. The border-line cases and carriers, unconscious of their heritage, complicate the problem. Public opinion is being aroused slowly but surely toward community responsibility for the sad injustice of a child being born of feeble-minded parents or being brought up by them. Complete solution of the problem may come only in a distant future, but, since no cures are known for feeble-mindedness, public opinion must be aroused to preventive measures already known and accepted.

Mental instability and insanity are occurrences which have not decreased markedly with improved mental hygiene and higher standards of living. Insanity occurs chiefly in persons past middle age. Since the survival of individuals over sixty-five is likely to increase greatly in the coming years (three-fold in forty years is the estimate given by experts), the proportion of mentally diseased persons will probably increase also. Hereditary factors in mental disease are far more difficult to ascertain than in physical traits. We know that in any human organism heredity contributes somewhat to the weakness or strength with which environmental stresses are met. We yield to or resist difficulties partly with the susceptibilities with which we are born, partly with the growth both of character and physique our surroundings have fostered. The large number of a patient's relatives who also suffer from schizophrenic and manic-depressive psychoses indicates the extent to which such disorders are possibly associated with hereditary tendencies in families.

There are types of insanity caused by alcoholism and by syphilis in which hereditary factors are hard to trace, if they exist. The weaknesses to which these causes are due may be genetic or they may be environmental. In either case, there is the possibility that these may be offset by stronger biological organisms or by better balanced mentality.

The seizures which give the chronic disease *epilepsy* its name are symptoms, rather than a disease itself, which ranks next to insanity in the suffering it involves. New methods of medication, however, with substantial help from the brain-wave electronic records called encephalograms, have brought the dawn of new hope for control and prevention of the seizures. Organizations for the education of the public and for the encouragement of research on the subject are active and give promise of fruitful work.

In our country, of the estimated five million persons suffering from serious incapacities due to genetic factors, at least two million of them are tragedies to themselves and their families and a heavy burden on society. The blind, the deaf, the crippled and some criminals who possess physical defects, need special types of education to meet their handicaps and sometimes also constant care. Such defects make a public health problem of enormous proportions and complexity. Its solution rests upon the medical profession and the public health authorities, backed by informed and intelligent public opinion. The only satisfactory method of approach, since no genetic defects can be cured, is *prevention—decreasing the number of defectives born.* Whether this shall be done by strict institutional care or the far more economical and humane one of sterilization, each state must decide. The latter involves no mutilation, no loss of function except the resulting infertility. New methods, which accomplish this end without operation and which are reversible, are being tested with encouraging results.

Racial problems arise from genetic factors in our population, resulting in differential birth rates among our races whose distinctive physical characteristics make assimilation difficult even if it were desirable—Negroes in our South, Indians in our reservations and Mexicans in our Southwest. These last two groups are doubling their numbers in each generation. We have no scientific evidence that these races differ from whites in their genetic capacity to develop qualities of social value, but certainly their present cultural level, their standards in education, in health and sanitation are such as to retard and complicate their own progress of development as well as that of the surrounding white groups. The same difficulties would exist in our South were not the birth rate greatly reduced among Negroes by the prevalence of diseases which cause sterility. If the present campaign, with new methods to combat these diseases, fulfills its promises, an increase in Negro births may be expected. Racial problems are accentuated by any tendency of smaller groups to increase over larger. A eugenic program will aim to equalize any disproportion now existing between whites, blacks, Mexicans and Indians. How this may be accomplished will await, perhaps, our solution of a related regional problem without the racial feature.

Regional problems which cause grave concern arise from differential birth rates in various regions of our country. With machinery so largely replacing man-power, farms can no longer absorb either their increasing population or their products. The Department of Agriculture has long been calling attention to the "depressing effects of high birth rates in poor rural areas." In cities, we find the largest families in crowded tenement houses. The birth rate among families on relief has exceeded that of the Nation as a whole. The excess of children is among those least able to care for them.

The old moral sanctions for large families—a high birth rate to offset a high death rate—are giving way to the new moral sanctions for family limitation proportionate to standards and resources. Family limitation has already proven (through private agencies) to be the wisest way to lift the unwanted burden of disproportionate births from the poor and ignorant. Public opinion must choose between a policy of informed, voluntary family limitation or an obligatory, tax-supported aid to such parents as are unable to provide minimum standards of housing, nutrition, and health for their young.

Among some groups, scientific contraception has long been used to solve personal or family problems by limiting the number of children for reasons of health, child-spacing, or economic resources. But this is only a method. Its use depends upon a sense of responsibility for the children to be born and also upon an acceptance of family limitation as part of the culture pattern of our country. Planned parenthood will be the basic means of building eugenic principles of *voluntary parenthood* from *sound stocks* into our evolving population policies. Without this factor, positive eugenics will remain static, theoretical, and ineffective.

So-called birth control, as a cause, has had a stormy career. Its issues have been clouded by natural and by organized obstacles to the spread of scientific information through private agencies or through health authorities, including doctors and nurses. Birth control has been unjustly charged with the aim of race suicide. *Planned parenthood,* a more constructive term, has supplanted it in general use and embodies the aim of race betterment. It works to encourage large families from fine stocks; to discourage any births from defective stocks; to reduce the long train of miseries resulting from unwanted births among those unable to provide for children; to establish voluntary parenthood.

Increase in births can best be brought about, not by restriction on contraceptive information and facilities, but by planning educational clinics and encouraging ideals which help parents to desire more children, and by forwarding measures which make it easier to give them a healthy upbringing.

The eugenic ideal of the human right to be *well born and well built* through wise care of character, health, education, recreation and economic security is basic in our democratic venture. Like our ideals of liberty and religious freedom, we are willing to fight to defend them. But we do not fight to impose them on others. We can only humbly point the way. Here is the path to true conservation of our most precious resource, the creation of individuals who alone can constitute the true grandeur of nations.

Many animals show a capacity to make a change in their

environment when it becomes unfavorable by moving away from it. Man's conscious thought has made it possible to change factors in the environment without the shift of location. The invention of raising food instead of hunting it may have been the first step. Slowly, primitive grains, fruits, vegetables, fungi, and animals were domesticated. Cooking developed, and the making of breads was followed by that of wines and cheeses. Food was only one field of invention; utensils, shelters, garments, textiles and transport developed. Man gradually learned to extend his muscular effort by the use of levers, wheels, and domestic animals. These activities and occupations *evolved,* but their significance lies in the continuance of man's evolution *through* them upon the new plane of mental evolution.

Extensive evolution of mind has taken place to provide such intentional changes in environment as are represented in present day clothing; in heating, lighting and air-conditioning systems for homes and other buildings; in man's development of natural resources; in his changing means of transportation with its air-conditioned trains and ships and its details of heaters, antifreeze and defrosters for automobiles, its oxygen supply for flyers above the stratosphere and superchargers for their engines; in the establishment of hospitals and control of infectious diseases; the new medicines, sun-lamps for health; vitamins to supplement even the best of diets; in the amenities and quickly evolving necessities of all the arts and sciences.

These inventions of men may be less basic than life's innovations of chlorophyll and haemoglobin, less triumphs of organization than the development of lungs for land-living animals and the precision movements of chromosomes and genes to secure heredity and variation; but they may still be regarded as life's achievements. Man's inventions and organizations, however, are the result of his conscious thought, which shifts the chief field of evolution to *human mind.*

Can you contemplate the changes which human minds have brought about in human life, without feeling that they are the expression of an evolving reality that has been behind the whole process of evolutionary progress and the dependable laws through which it has worked?

In human evolution the appearance of conscious thought was a new level. The established mechanisms of sense organs, nervous system with brain, which adjusted the activity of muscles to surrounding conditions, had new factors to reckon with when conceptual thought dawned and language was born.

Was what Wilson calls the "miraculous birth of language" due to chance or was it the thrust of some minded reality, lifting the processes of human evolutionary progress to a new mental level where mind was implemented by language and both mind and its means of expression could evolve? The non-spatial realm of human thought gave a new field of activity. As was the case in the radical change to man's erect posture, new difficulties arose; situations and results might be new in quality. Old structures were used but new laws were operative; new tempos became possible. Words became storehouses not only for visible objects and acts but also for *invisible feelings.* Intangibles could be shared. Since then, mankind has always needed the great prayer from Phaedrus, "May the outward and the inward man be at one."

If you have watched the dawn of consciousness and of conceptual thought in an infant and the later growth of association, language and reason in the child, you have the pattern of the probable development of these characteristic activities in the human race. In the long history of evolutionary processes the step to conscious thought was comparatively recent. It was a momentous step, working great changes, but its chief results are doubtless still to come. The marvel of its new plane of activity is often overlooked. To only a favored few is thinking a source of pleasure or profit. The effort required is met by the usual lag opposing new demands on old structures. It suggests the need of a more intelligent use of the processes of education and a more broadly philosophical grasp of its aims.

Education in the United States has been a responsibility of the state for many years, but recently the younger and the older age levels are receiving added attention. Nursery schools, kindergartens, classes for the subnormal and some special groups for the most gifted are taking care of youngsters, while extension courses, adult education, more scholarships and adjusted entrance requirements to colleges and state universities provide more generously for older groups.

Perhaps the greatest change of all has come through the recognition of the need for recreational facilities used largely by children in family groups. The National Recreation Association, through its literature and its training of leaders for both city and country, has expressed its conviction that "families that play together stay together." Parks, tennis and basketball courts, football and baseball fields, public golf courses, dams which impound water to provide swimming in summer, skating and hockey in winter, and other resources, such as bathing beaches and safe boating, coasting reservations and ski trails have come into appreciated use. Many of these listed activities originated in towns or counties and were then taken over by the states.

The United States as a country has been slow to feel that the individual deserved and sometimes required the help of his community. It can no longer be said, however, that our government spends more on pigs than on people. The large proportion spent for old age security is due to the fact that while modern science is prolonging the life span, industry is shortening the period of employment. Modern industrial society does not provide subsistence for the aged. Does it provide maintenance at the other end of the life span? Children cost much more now than when eighty per cent of our people lived on farms and the feeding of children meant outlay of time and effort rather than money.

Whatever we may think of the wisdom and the future of these paternalistic, centralized activities of government, the measures have come about through the recognition of social needs and are aimed at the conservation of human values. They are all intended to help environmental factors in the lives of our people. Such benefits as they may add to the growth and development of our country's children may *aid,* but in no way *replace* well-born parents, willing, as of old, to work hard, to make sacrifices, to develop their own growing intelligence as well as that of their children, to cherish the old moralities in new applications to a changing world. The eugenic program under whatever type of government will always aim to encourage independence, to strengthen character and to develop balanced personalities.

How far is the human individual responsible for his own development, and thus, for his own share in shaping the curve of human evolution? Human lives are mixed together in a vast network made from the interweaving of various strands of genes, not in any one plane, but radiating in all directions in an ever-enlarging sphere. Looking at it from outside, you can understand that the knots formed by unions at intersections may give rise to new strands. You are not surprised that different knots should have characteristic peculiarities and also form new strands that are unique. But can you put yourself, with your whole range and detail of experience, without which to you the entire universe might be non-existent, in a relation of identity to one—just one—of all the billions of knots tied from the strands of the past? Are you so much a product of gene combination that if that knot had never existed you would never have existed? What is the relation of the physical gene combination that is yours to the conscious self that *is you?* Is there something for which genes cannot account? Is there some reality of self into which gene combinations enter and whose interaction with environment determines the individuality of selves?

Modern psychology tends to supplant the term *self* with the term *personality,* defining it variously as a total outcome of an individual's mental organization, comprising all his permanent mental conditions and organized experiences at any period of life. But personality seems to be dynamic—the result of the "interaction of all psychophysical systems within an individual which determine his unique adjustment to the environment." The significance of the word *self* for many is this dynamic factor, the determining agent of adaptation which implies responsibilities. Is there a *self-determined you* in combination with the *you* brought about by your heritage of genes? Are you limited in your possibilities by your gene actualities or can you use your unique gene birthright *creatively?* The reality behind the phrase "the dignity of man" is based not only on man's unique capacities but on his responsibility for the use he makes of them. You can supposedly do nothing to change the genes. You are outfitted with them "for better or for worse." Are the educational processes of your home, your school, your church, your community, your country responsible for all your characteristics not determined by genes? Or is there a free self which chooses how it shall be built? Biology takes invisible genes on faith and proves them by experiment but has nothing definite to say about selves except that each is a center of life and that they vary.

Scientific psychology's rapid advance has been largely due to what it has learned from the body. It ventures no assumptions about freedom of the will. It is not ready to say that man is more than an object in nature because he is more than a fact. Facts are not conscious of facts; the self is. Facts to themselves have no value; the human self has values. These values shift with experience; but you act at any time in view of the values and meanings facts hold for you. Self comes to feel that it *is* a value; that it has a meaning and a worth beyond the bare facts of its existence. There may be tides of circumstance which no one can withstand, but the way the self takes such happenings is more important than the thing that happens. To many thoughtful people the universe seems to have a meaning. If it has, *you* will eventually come to understand your relation to it, its vast realities, its long evolutionary history and its future possibilities. *You* have a standing in the universe. You alone have the self-knowledge which will tell you whether or not reaction experiments, conditioned responses, and curves of learning reveal the essence of yourself and express your value.

Both biology and psychology have one source of evidence about selves not to be overlooked in considering the distinctness of individuals. In the case of identical twins, the initial gene combination is believed to divide into two separate parts at a very early stage in its development, giving rise to two distinct individuals. You might easily expect more precise likenesses than really exist in such twins. They have the same eye color, the same hair texture; their fingerprints and also their toe prints, with occasional exceptions, are identical. The remarkable thing is not that they are very like each other; not that there are recognizable differences between them; but that they are actually two distinct persons, two identifiable selves, who, while they often say the same thing in the same way at the same time, and may spell backward the same words when they are writing in separate rooms, may still have very different dispositions, reacting very differently to life's stresses and strains, its joys and sorrows. Under no circumstances could you find two individuals whose developmental conditions are so nearly alike. They are of the same sex, age, and have the same heritage of genes; yet the *selves* may be very unlike.

There is no moment when, either as parent or as offspring,

we are conscious of a self being transmitted, either from within or without. Is it like the body, something first given, then built by yourself? Your body develops in a general ancestral type of structure, using, in a manner determined by the genes, whatever materials are at hand. You learn your body and come to dominate it. You fit it to your uses. What it does, *you* do. It is a symbol to others of what you *are* and of what you value. Is there a reality of *self* which evolves, or is the process mere development?

With the development of the science of electronics, the atom bomb, and the concept of the constitution of all matter as electrical, new vision has come to the general public of the possible future evolution of mind. It is undoubtedly the chief arena of present-day evolution, but the curve of its progress is still to be determined. Can we direct or control this curve?

There has been a great increase in knowledge and in the means of integrating knowledge. Any age, rich in the successes of science, is hindered by their very bulk in making them a unity. Our present-day triumphs in control over nature in the fields of theoretical and applied science are in strong contrast to our failures in ordering our own lives as evidenced by our personal tragedies and by the world's wars and disunities. Apparently, faith that there is latent order in this seeming chaos has to come from within; it is not apparent from daily experience. Hugh Stott Taylor writes:

> Science is an intellectual technique; it can never be a moral dynamic. Science occupies a sure place in the hierarchy of knowledge but it can never hold the supreme place. Its great contributions can be used both for good and for evil.[46]

Science is not responsible for the uses to which it is put. Man determines that. Thinking is the needed moral dynamic.

The level of man's mental activity can continue to be raised along the lines of mental energy, acuteness and range of perception, trustworthiness of memory, clarity of thought and expression, synthetic grasp and intuitiveness, analytical capacity, creative imagination and balance of judgment, sympathy and compassion; but if these are to have a part in man's evolution they must be secured by deliberate purpose in personal and public education. We know more than we did about how minds work; but there is little agreement as to the *ends for which they should work.* To give direction to human evolution we must have an aim. Mental activity as man's latest implement for his evolution is not something fixed and finite, but, like every other factor in the evolutionary process, is subject to modification, improvements or degenerations.

The truly significant controls for man to establish are not those of environment alone but those of his own mental states, his independence of stimulants, the adjustment of his emotional conflicts, his steadiness of purpose, his range of sympathy, his capacity to put himself in the "other fellow's place," his disinterestedness and unselfish concern for others, his spiritual perceptions. He needs to know what values and meaning he wishes life to hold, then shape his life to secure them. Aims or their lack are in constant control of man's present-day evolution. You are a part of the problem involved or a part of its solution; you cannot be both. Powerful leverage is required to bring the latent order of a durable peace out of the chaos of clashing nationalisms in our evolving world. This can come only through the possession of a heart of peace in each individual developing in these troubled times.

Centuries ago Archimedes said, "Give me a lever that is long enough and a place on which to stand and I can move the whole world." Our ideals of education are high; our buildings and laboratories are incomparable. As levers these ideals should prove long enough. But our commitment to them—the place on which we stand—do our convictions falter? Are we on firm ground? The results suggest the shifting sands of self-sufficiency rather than the eternal rock of God's purpose and the availability of His power. Our lives make transparently clear the values by which we live and the depth of our dedication to them.

CHAPTER THIRTEEN

Are Science and Religion at Odds?

The function of religion in human life may well be the completion of the unfinished world-view of science, for while science deals with facts, religion and philosophy are chiefly concerned with the *value and meaning of facts,* which science taken alone would omit.

The business of science is to discover facts and the relations between them so that men may understand the world and use it for their ends. Science has little to say about what these ends shall be, or which are worth pursuing.

Religion works for discernment by each individual of his personal relation to the whole of things—the most real, the eternal—but regards this whole as a region of value rather than fact. Religion with its values is like light, itself invisible, but making all other values visible.

Philosophy centers its interest on what reason can do for meaning and consistency in the whole—to satisfy the whole man.

Religion has aimed to meet the needs of the heart of mankind with its intuitions and its spiritual hungers.

In his Gifford Lectures, Dixon said:

> We know more than ever was known and are convinced that we know nothing of what we most wish to know. We distrust more utterly than has ever been mistrusted the very intellect which has achieved so many and so signal triumphs . . .
>
> The failure of science, as anyone can see, is its failure to minister to the needs of the soul. The failure of religion lies, on the other hand, in its inability to meet the needs of the intellect, to answer the innumerable questions we ask ourselves and must ask ourselves.[47]

Religion is indebted to science for the continuously stretched horizons and resulting forward steps. Has religion had any balancing contribution to make to science? The relation is perhaps more difficult to see. The rapid development of science has impressed us with the elements of change and relativity, and has resulted in some activities carried on merely for the sake of change and relativity.

Religion has aimed to keep alive individual discrimination between the eternal and the outworn or outmoded; between the truth of values and the values of truth. Religion has held firmly to its belief in a divine thread in human history, not imposed from outside, but arising from within human minds.

Religion has seen that the most important events in a living history take place in human minds; they are decisions. Influenced as these are by motives, by passions, by values, they are not provable facts, nor can their presence and effectiveness be measured alone by observable results. To religion, ideas are the most effective forces in the world. They may keep on working long after their obvious power has disappeared. Their reality, like their power, being unverifiable, may escape the scientific historian.

The advance of physical science has compelled men repeatedly to revise their ideas of such matters as the universe, their explanations of planetary motion, their estimates of the age of the earth, their beliefs about the origin of the human species, their ideas about atoms, the relations of matter-energy, and their inferences that human history can be known only through a record of provable facts. The natural and wise reluctance of men to accept new views until they have been proved to be true views, and the prolonged disagreement about implications of the evolution theory, have led to the so-called conflict between science (evolution) and religion as set forth in the Bible. It is now easy to see that this controversy has been not so much between evolution and religion as between ancient and modern scientific views of nature and creation. But has this point of view brought a complete truce?

Because of their Book, Judaism and Christianity have always been counted among the world's learned religions. Someone has said that it takes *learning* to sift out the chaff of Hebrew contemporary thought, such as the Cosmology of Moses, from the kernel of truth wrapped within it. But great spiritual truths are in that Book. As a cumulative record during long centuries of the discoveries of the human spirit about its relation to God, it can never be discarded.

By the beginning of the twentieth century, the peoples of Europe had generally ceased to be troubled by the scientific discrepancies of the Bible or by the supposed implications of the theory of evolution. Higher criticism, reverent and scholarly, has taken the edge from belief in the verbal inerrancy of the scriptures. In America, however, the opposition of fundamentalists to evolution in a few states resulted in legislation (1925) against the teaching of evolution in the state-supported institutions of those states. Consequently, the idea still prevails in many parts of the United States that choice must be made between evolution and religion, since the two are assumed to be incompatible. The fundamentalist takes literally Biblical statements which to most people seem stated metaphorically. As to the *details* of the origin of species, the Book of Genesis is significantly silent. Nothing is said there, however, which excludes the possibility that evolution is a process of creation. The Hebrew conception of the universe was naive, and, in the light of recent discoveries, wholly untenable. The religious value of the Bible, however, does not depend upon its scientific accuracy in astronomy, geology, and biology.

Science and religion have to do with different fields of human experience. The physical sciences attempt to explain observed facts in mechanistic terms. The basis of religion is found in man's capacity to appreciate spiritual values and to be loyal to them. It is as futile to charge evolution with atheism as to make that charge against the theory of the gene, or the atomic theory. Evolution is no substitute for God. Many regard it as God's dynamic way of working. The theory of evolution is not to be understood as an attempt to explain the order of nature or the original constitution of the universe. Nor does it attempt to decide the metaphysical problem of what sort of "stuff" the universe in reality consists. It does not answer the ancient query of "God or no God?" Evolution is a creative process, whereby new types of organisms are produced.

Here is a page from the *Autobiography* of Robert A. Millikan, first published in *Science* in 1923.

> We, the undersigned, deeply regret that in recent controversies there has been a tendency to present science and religion as irreconcilable and antagonistic domains of thought, for in fact they meet distinct human needs, and in the rounding out of human life they supplement rather than displace or oppose each other.
>
> *The purpose of science is to develop, without prejudice or preconception of any kind, a knowledge of the facts, the laws, and the processes of nature. The even more important task of religion, on the other hand, is to develop the consciences, the ideals, and the aspirations of mankind.* Each of these two activities represents a deep and vital function of the soul of man, and both are necessary for the life, the progress, and the happiness of the human race.
>
> It is a sublime conception of God which is furnished by science, and one wholly consonant with the highest ideals of religion, when it represents Him as revealing Himself through countless ages in the development of the earth as an abode for man and in the age-long inbreathing of life into its constituent matter, culminating in man with his spiritual nature and all his Godlike powers.[48]

The statement is signed by sixteen of our most distinguished religious leaders, by fifteen top scientists and by fourteen great men of affairs.

Modern religion and religious scientists, then, think of God as the mind, intelligence and will, whose creative activity is expressed in all the phenomena of nature traced by science in its work. It believes the universe not only created by the divine will, but momentarily supported by the perpetually creative activity of that will. All the phenomena of nature are manifestations of that activity and the uniformity of natural law the consistent, steady operation of that will. These laws have all the austerity and all the benevolence of nature. They may crush us as well as sustain and restore us. But Hebrew consciousness of the presence of God and the search for His guidance remain as the dominant influence in modern religious thought.

On the north rim of the Grand Canyon, a group of eager listeners had heard the ranger-naturalist's masterly exposition of the formation of the mile-deep mass of rock—its repeated up-liftings and down-wearings, its three submergences beneath the sea where new deposits of sediment with living forms gave the successive fossil records—before the mighty Colorado began its slow cutting of the incredible gorge. As we filed mutely back from the profound experience, my attention focussed on a disconsolate figure seated on a rock, once more surveying the vast spectacle.

"You look discouraged," I said. "What's the trouble?"

"What I'd like to know," she answered with no preliminaries to me, a complete stranger, "is where does God come in?"

The modern answer is that God doesn't come in at all. He is already and always in! To me the deepest truth in the world is this *incarnation of the World Spirit* in the *facts of sense*. It is impossible for anyone who has breathed the spirit of modern science to believe in an absentee God, whose will is external to that which it has made. The mature thought of God conceives of Him as the intelligence working in and through natural law. When a scientist seems to leave God out, it may be because the *world as a whole* is not the field of his science, or it may be because the scientist is a mechanist who accepts strict determinism as final, excluding all causes and purposes.

In this, we touch the heart of today's most fundamental conflict between science and religion. Science, which deals with facts, needs to consider no final causes, no purposes to accomplish its work. Science tries to find out how things operate, not what they are for; to know their ways and to explain them without asking for ultimate causes.

Some scientists, having no use for values nor purposes to explain their work, assume that the laws of chemistry and physics rule all happenings and that, therefore, there can be no values nor meanings in the universe. But *why* the reverential attitude of the scientist toward his own work, his scientific conscience, scrupulous truthfulness, disciplined exactness and lifelong devotion, if there are no meanings or purposes? Why fight against totalitarianism if we and our opponents are helpless automata? Why believe in democracy if its distinctive quality, the worth of the individual, and the moral responsibility of each person for his decisions and his acts, cannot qualify as true in the crucible of science? The mastery of our material environment may lead us to disaster unless the nothingness of matter has a right relation to the allness of mind, of law, of world spirit.

The question, *What is religion?* has been variously answered. Religion, like life, is difficult to define and for the same reason—its bewildering variety of forms. Religion appears to be one thing in St. Peter's in Rome and quite another in the jungles of Africa or in a Shinto temple.

Religion is an attitude toward existence and destiny but certainly not a church, nor a creed, nor a political system. As expressions of religion, churches and creeds are not to be ignored; but they are not religion. Some think that Micah gave the best definition of religion when he asked, "What does God require of thee, but to do justly, to love mercy, and to walk humbly with thy God?" Religion, therefore, is a way of life—the living of one's life in the consciousness of a relation to God and of an obligation to one's fellow men. If Micah is right, religion begins with a firsthand personal psychological experience. The roots of religious experience grow in the soil of appreciation of spiritual values. Religion, therefore, has its foundations in emotion as well as in the intellect and reason.

Man has been considered by some persons as "incurably religious." But the modern thought seems to be, as stated by naturalism, "Man is a praying animal; scare him enough and he prays, revealing something deep in subconsciousness and therefore highly authentic." That such questionably anthropological facts may be the basis of contemporary religious belief would indicate that science has been enthroned in place of more accepted religious realities. It would indicate that such religion has no truth of its own on which to rest its case.

What we call man's place in nature is always relevant to religion. Out of what do we, self-conscious, thinking human beings come? What are we doing here? Whither do we go?

What comes after the death and disintegration of the body of each one of us?

Opposed to the naturalists, stand the idealists, the religionists, and the religious scientists who may hold both of these latter positions since they are not mutually exclusive. To each of these groups, everything in the universe is subordinate to mind. They assume, therefore, that nothing in the world can be meaningless because mind acts always in view of meanings. Human beings as among the things of the world must have a meaning. They have been evolved by a cosmic process which might indicate a nature due a certain importance. If there are values, as most of us believe, they cannot be contrary to cosmic values. In our appreciations of values, we come close to an immediate grasp of the ultimate sense of existence, the sum of which can never be zero.

Refusing to be engulfed by the naturalists' mechanistic flood of meaninglessness, their opponents maintain that values *exist;* that they are *true.* In all humility, they cannot accept themselves as puppets with no moral responsibility. Nor can they think of science or of religion as other than growing *bodies of truth.* Some of these beliefs endure; some are discarded, having served to light up new paths. Idealists point out that the greatness of science with its mechanistic method of work is measured by the *meaning* of its facts; the *worth* of its discoveries; the *significance* of its cumulative body of truth. The spirit of science, which many regard as its supreme contribution to human life, is very like the religious spirit. Both lead men to give what is best in themselves to something greater than themselves. Both have challenged many of the finest minds of our age. Both groups may say:

"God upon our lifted foreheads
Pours the boon of endless quest."

In the creative work of artists, architects, poets, musicians, writers, a sense of the whole comes first, relations of details being worked out later. But with science, wholes are usually built up from parts. These wholes are so intricate, so diverse, so vast that each field shuts out the others. What can a zoologist know of astrophysics; the geologist, of enzymes, hormones, and genes; the astronomer, of vitamins and viruses; the botanist, of radioactivity and atom smashing? They may all keep well informed about the significance of work in other fields than their own, but the infinite detail, so patiently worked out in all, is beyond inclusion in any one lifetime.

This is one reason why scientists, as such, have little to say about the world as a whole or a world-view. This field is the special inquiry of philosophy; but its results belong to us all. As men, we may have deep convictions about life as a whole and about the place of God and religion in the world. Newton, whom Locke regarded as the greatest theologian of his time, thought more highly of his own contribution to theology than to science. Now as theories of gravitation give way to relativity, philosophical scientists come back to Newton's conception of the world as a thought in the mind of God. Einstein writes, "Enough for me to contemplate the mystery of conscious life perpetuating itself through all eternity to reflect upon the marvelous structure of the universe which we can dimly perceive and strive humbly to understand even an infinitesimal part of the intelligence in nature." [49] He does not tell us whether, to him, only mind is intelligent or if he assumes mind behind all "intelligence in nature." Eddington says in *Nature of the Physical World,* "There are some to whom the sense of a divine presence irradiating the soul is one of the most obvious things in experience. In their view a man without this sense is to be regarded as we regard a man without a sense of humor. The absence is a kind of mental deficiency . . . and as laughter cannot be compelled by the scientific exposition of the structure of a joke, so a philosophic discussion of the attributes of God (or an impersonal substitute) is likely to miss the intimate response of the spirit which is the central point of the religious experience." [50]

Millikan—Nobel Prize winner in physics (1923)—writes in *Science and Life:* "There have been two great influences in the history of the world which have made goodness the outstanding characteristic in the conception of God. The first influence was Jesus of Nazareth; the second influence has been the growth of modern science and particularly the growth of the theory of evolution. . . . Let me then henceforth use the word God to describe *that which is behind the mystery of existence and that which gives meaning to it.* I think you will not misunderstand me, then, when I say that I have never known a thinking man who did not believe in God." [51] Is there not room in our world for both science and religion, and of philosophy to join them? The continual analysis of the relation of the ultimate activities of science to the progress of the race is essential.

It would indeed indicate a meager religious insight if, in a century rich in intellectual growth, we found no changes in our conceptions of religious experiences. The bases of all such experiences belong to the eternal, unchangeable things. Our ideas have continually to be revised to fit new discoveries. The new frontiers are far removed from the old. The forms of religion may evolve, but their function is always the same: to bring men face to face with the everlasting and the real.

Kant thought *conscience* the one point of experience in which we touch absolute reality. He regarded it as a token of something in man above nature, for it calls on him to control his own natural impulses, instincts, aversions and desires and *not be controlled by them*—to govern them rather than be governed by them. To Kant, as to many religious thinkers, conscience is the Call of Reality within the individual mind, allying us with a reality deeper than the flow of natural events. This inherent basis of morality was the Greek idea and one of the reasons why Plato identified morality with the control of the appetites by reason. Christianity taught that morality was not inherent in mankind, but imposed by God; in its teachings it added the elements of love and sympathy, to reason. It takes a fusion of belief in the intrinsic value of morality with these other roots of morality to satisfy the modern mind and conscience.

Conscience is variable because our sense of unity with the deeper reality fluctuates. That this sense needs renewal from time to time is a matter of experience. Out of this need, observances have become established which are acts of deliberate attention to this relationship. Worship, meditation, communion, ritual, prayer have as their purpose the *resensitizing* of the self to its unity with the Real.

The superficial evolutionary view that conscience is an hereditary relic of ancient punishments is questioned. Mental traits handed down from ancestors grow fainter as they recede from their source. Evidence supports the belief that conscience grows more sensitive as the race evolves. Since it moves ahead of ancestral requirements, can it be explained away as mere biological inheritance?

Religion is not in a compartment shut away from the rest of our mental life. Religion must evolve as do all products of human thought. There must be changes in every living religious system, not in its core, but in its expressions, in its adjustment to the growing body of scientific truth and to the changes in the whole of our world-view. Religion is still the trustworthy moral dynamic.

Science is giving a new and universal background to all religious faiths that persist in our world. Against this common background, they will have to maintain themselves. Each must be related to all established thought and knowledge. That type of religion will best survive which has the best coherence with a world-view, the most satisfying interpretation for mind and feeling, the most inspiring motive for worthy living.

Religion has passed beyond the bitter conflict with the scientific-consciousness of the race. We have entered a stage of maturity where a *free science,* a *free philosophy* and a *free religion* are united and complementary factors in a complete world-view. These three overlap and intermesh, meeting different human needs and supplementing one another. Science, philosophy and religion differ in what they emphasize, each making an essential contribution to the guidance of life, not as opponents, but as partners.

Religion today faces a powerful opponent in a new science of government—the completely secularized state. Why did Soviet, Nazi, Nipponese and Fascist economic policies seem to present a nearly solid front against religion? Taking first from men their right to sell their labor freely when and where they will, making it a criminal offense for workers to strike, they established compulsory labor. This is the first step toward reintroduction of slavery. The process begins by attacks on Christian faith. One of the basic beliefs of Christianity is the worth of the individual and the moral responsibility of each human being for his decisions and his acts. These are the ideas which have put an end to old slaveries. They must be removed before new slaveries and the subordination of the individual to the state can come to pass and be established.

Certain Marxian doctrines assume that science and industry, economics and psychology, furnish everything needed for the guidance of life. This rouses a ready response in the secular-minded everywhere the world over. Why should religion be needed as an implement to help in managing a life? It is hard for youth to wait to see what things *mean,* in terms of what they *lead to.* It is easy to yield to the common drag toward paganism and indifference; natural to rebel against traditional patterns and ancient sanctions; and usual to find obscure, the role of religion in matters affecting individual and social conscience. To enter combat with a totalitarian positivism, we need to muster not *blind allegiance* to our beliefs, but *reasoned understanding* of their sources and implications. We need also to understand the sources of opposing beliefs—and the fervor of the loyalty of their adherents.

Is religion an inherent need in the nature of man? In establishing a new world order, is religion needed permanently to keep it sound? Does all that is valid in morals need something of the nature of religion to give it full effect in the human will? These are the questions whose answers matter more than they have ever mattered before in human history.

To deal with such questions, every religion needs to know and to stand upon the common ground of all religions. There is at the core of all creeds a nucleus of religious truth, for they have all come from the religious intuitions of mankind. Without this nucleus of reality, Christianity or any other religion would find nothing on which to build. At the heart of all the piety in the world, however vague and wistful, however encrusted with superstition, however be-meaned by self-seeking bargaining with its gods, or however exalted, there is this germ, this inalienable religious intuition of the human soul about the reality of God. Any theory of the nature of man, any form of government, totalitarian or democratic, which excludes religion from the needs of man finds itself facing substitutes. If the intuition of the reality of God is derided, men tend to enshrine a Leader or a myth in their hearts, in their world order, in their morals. The lastingness of such substitutes is yet to be proved.

There are myths which belong to the permanent insights of mankind. Such is the hope of a coming human brotherhood. I believe this hope is based on a literal reality—a reality as unobtrusive as breathing, as natural and effortless as being alive, the truth that the world is a *self* with its own unity and *living purpose,* the truth of the existence of God. We may think and work in harmony with this truth and its cosmic demands—or in opposition to it. Thus our convictions and our efforts may increase order or disorder. We need a belief in something constant and unchangeable.

With the existence of God as its central fact, a universal religion does not have to be established; it exists. Around this nucleus, a much simpler religion than any now formulated may grow. Such a religion, unobscured by varying doctrines, is already a living religion in many hearts. It is a more universal, less contentious, less expressive religion than any we have known. Some call it the religion of the modern man, but it is patterned after Micah's ancient formula—a way of life, lived with a consciousness of a relation to God and of an obligation to one's fellow men. This is perhaps the religious aspect of the coming pattern of world-culture.

Though the world is a world of natural law, not invented by man, but discovered by him through science, so too it is a world of reason formulated by philosophy—and also it is a world of moral law disclosed to man through religion. The supreme law of the world is not physical but moral. Man, not matter, is the chief problem of the world. Both men and societies have their reality in this inner moral quality, not in wealth nor in force. It is this moral power which governs their destiny.

CHAPTER FOURTEEN

What of Life After Death?

We have been considering various problems centering about man's life, his place in nature and the question, "Out of what have we self-conscious, thinking human beings come?" We now venture to ask, "What comes after death?" Is death the end for human selves as it is for their bodies?

We are sure that death brings dissolution of all the mechanisms of stimulus and response and of the mind as an object in nature, subject to the laws of cause and effect as are other objects. But as for the free, spontaneous self which uses these mechanisms for its own ends, which is purposive and value-judging, which gives rise to a series of deeds that can never be explained by mechanisms, does this too pass into oblivion?

Dixon in *The Human Situation* says,

> Immortality is a word which stands for the stability and permanence of that unique and precious quality we dis-

> cern in the soul which, if lost, leaves nothing worth preservation in the world. If you can find in it no such quality its preservation cannot of course interest you, and you can accept the thought of its destruction with equanimity. And in this tranquil acquiescence is thus summed up your opinion of all existence as a worthless misery.[52]

In a questionnaire sent out some decades ago to a selected group of American men of science, Professor Leuba tried to discover whether scientific training tended to make men skeptical in regard to religious beliefs, especially belief in God and immortality. Somewhat to his surprise he found that a greater number believed in life for the individual after death than believed in a personal God. Is this traditional belief in immortality based on reason or on authority? On what grounds is the belief in immortality accepted?

William James, in a reply to a questionnaire regarding religious beliefs sent out in 1904 by James B. Pratt, answered the two questions on this matter characteristically as follows: *Do you believe in personal immortality?* "Never keenly; but more strongly as I grow older." *If so, why?* "Because I'm just getting fit to live."

To those who accept naturalism as a philosophy there can obviously be no question of survival of personality after death. To such persons, the disintegration of the body spells the extinction of the individual. A well-known criminal lawyer, Clarence Darrow, once told a large audience in Boston Symphony Hall that all the essential constituents of a man could be bought for ninety-eight cents at a drugstore. "It has been estimated," he said, "that the average individual contains enough fat to make seven bars of soap, enough iron for one nail, enough sugar to fill a small shaker, enough lime to whitewash a chicken-coop, enough phosphorus for twenty-two hundred match-heads, enough magnesium for one dose of magnesia, and enough sulphur to rid a dog of fleas." How much more a man is worth than his ingredients! Darrow's argument would seem to show that he had not located the human being at all, even on the commercial level. For it is hard business which pays its thousands per year for these ninety-eight cent men, one of whom received recently in one year $1,500,000 bonus in addition to his regular salary of $100,000.

To anyone who can see in human personality only what can be found by chemical analysis, the notion of life after death seems wholly fantastic. The case for immortality seems no better if it is tried in the court of the dissecting room. The anatomist finds no more evidence of immortality than does the chemist. If there is "more in man than the breath of his body" the case of immortality must be tried in a higher court than that of physical science. The persistence of the chemical elements which compose the human being is not immortality. If there is nothing more in human personality than can be expressed in terms of chemistry, it is idle to talk about survival after death.

But many persons who cannot accept a belief in the survival of death by human personality admit a kind of immortality in the obvious fact that one's influence lives on for a time in the lives of others. Man has been able to extend the basis of this possible influence beyond death in many ways. First by speech, then far more by writing, and more again by printing, he has passed on for others his contribution to the experience and knowledge of his time. More recently through photography, projection and sound reproduction, he has greatly increased the range and detail of such records and the ease of their duplication and distribution (what Kaempffert calls "Electronic Immortality" in *Science Today and Tomorrow*). On tiny films, every great book of all the ages throughout the world can now be gathered under one roof and, page by page, be projected by the student as need arises. As a permanent record of current happenings, many of our nation's newspapers now use Recordax, by means of which a whole month's issue of the thickest daily in the world can be transferred to three reels of film, reels not much larger than a pack of cigarettes. Such extension of one's self, character, thought, times, and creative works is not, however, to be confused with the possible continuance of a human personality after the passing of its body.

Science, as such, concedes one kind of immortality in the patiently worked-out story of the continuity of life's germ plasm from generation to generation, from age to age. The organism reproduces itself in other organisms which possess the same self-reproducing capacity, so that a given organism at any moment contains within itself one of the conditions for an unending series of like organisms extending on in endless time. This perpetuation of pattern—living on through our descendants—however true, is a very different matter from being able to continue one's personal adventure as an individual after death.

Some believe that the evidence collected by the Society of Psychical Research demonstrates survival of personality after death. Professor Podmore, Sir Arthur Conan Doyle, and

Sir Oliver Lodge believed that, notwithstanding proof of trickery by some mediums, evidence of survival obtained at some seances is trustworthy. They asserted that communication with the dead has been proved. Professor William McDougall, however, like most men of scientific training, remained unconvinced by these claims. Since his death, however, there have been experiences of communication with the dead reported by sincere and scientific persons which, like phases of supersensible physics, imply the use of human awareness-mechanisms beyond the range of usual sense perceptions. Bergson accepted intuitions as truths which we *know,* not by *feeling sure* about them, but by perception of their actual presence. He views intuitions as perceptions of invisible, intangible, imponderable but nonetheless actual realities, *known* through an extension of sense perception to regions beyond habitual reach of our senses.

It is claimed by others that the longing for immortality is an instinct and as such attests its own truth—that is, the fact of immortality. Instinct, it is asserted, supplements reason as a key to truth. Under natural conditions instincts may be trusted not to mislead. If a young golden plover has the instinct to launch out from Nova Scotia over the Atlantic to the South, it is certain that there is a land to the South which can be reached before the bird's store of fuel fat is exhausted. Were the plover to trust its reason instead of instinct, it would doubtless decide that the risks of the journey were too great and that it would be better to play safe and remain where there was plenty of food. As a result, he would probably perish of cold and starvation in a Nova Scotia winter. In some instances instincts appear more trustworthy than reason. So also possibly the instinct for immortality. That the desire for life after death is a true instinct has, however, not been demonstrated. Some find it based not on an instinct or longing for survival, but on an incapacity of the mind to conceive of its own extinction, which is an altogether different thing. To be an instinct, any drive which influences behavior must be shared by all individuals of the species. It is doubtful that a universal human-longing for continued life can be demonstrated. Perhaps the longing for immortality is after all but a projection of the biological "will to live" and to perpetuate the individual and the race —a part of the impulse of youth for the affirmation of life. If so, it would have no significance in relation to survival after death.

Toward any argument from analogy our attitude is properly one of skepticism. This, however, does not imply that analogical argument is without weight.

Many believe that the case for immortality is strengthened by analogy. The crisis of death, it is asserted, is no more serious than other crises which the individual survives. One crisis, for example, arises when the ovum leaves the ovary and consequently is no longer nourished and protected there. Deprived of these conditions, the persistence of the life of the ovum seems a remote possibility. Only if the egg is fertilized and becomes implanted in the uterus will it survive the catastrophe of ovulation. Another crisis occurs when a child is born. To the unborn child the chances that he could survive separation from the mother's body would seem remote. How could this organism, which for months leads an aquatic life, live out of fluid? Survival of the crisis of death, it is urged, seems no more unlikely. Unfortunately for the analogy, the earlier crises are physical. Physical survival, however, is not assumed in the case of immortality. What survives death is not the body, but a soul, a mind, a personality. Just as the human embryo, living in fluid is prepared before birth by the development of lungs and sense organs for a new life in the untried medium of air, may it not be that we are prepared before death by a growing sensitiveness to spiritual values for a new life in an untried medium of whose nature we can only surmise and can only think of as a condition for continuing growth and evolution?

But there is another analogy which deserves our attention; for it represents another type of crisis which throws light on the meaning of the whole scene of evolution—it is the crisis when quantitative change becomes qualitative, as when, from a solution of increased concentration, crystals suddenly form. It was this type of analogy which Fiske used in his Ingersoll Lecture on Immortality when he pictured the "transformations of the conic sections of the ellipse as the two foci spread farther apart, and then the bursting of the ellipse into the parabola, whose infinite limbs never return to enclose a space, but move forever outward, toward the parallel. So," he proposed, "by continuous change, nature may have produced in man a creature whose curve of life is not drawn back at last into the gravitation of the dust but passes outward on an endless quest." [53]

Can logic settle the question of human survival of death? If we look next at the logical analysis of the problem, we are turned at once to the wider world-view of the matter which takes it out of the region of probability or improbability where for most contemporary thinkers it seems to lie. The common judgment referred to in the chapter on "The Relation of Mind and Body" is that, because of the close association of mind and brain, survival of death is improbable. But this is fuzzy thinking! If there is a strict co-variation between brain action and mental action, survival is not improbable but impossible. The element of doubt attaches, not to the inference, but to the reasoning which sets up the premise—the accepted co-variation. If that premise is not true, the exclusion of survival fails, not by gradual steps, but completely. There are no intermediate degrees of probability.

Our world-view of survival shows us that it is neither probable nor improbable in advance of deciding about this world-view and its metaphysics. For metaphysics undertakes to determine what sorts of order or disorder exist in our world; and it is on the ground of these types of order that probability of any sort has to be judged. One type may exclude survival; another may require it; a third may show survival to be possible under certain conditions. In no case are we dealing with probabilities.

As a matter of human history, those who affirm immortality have usually been more hopeful than certain, whereas those who deny it seem to regard their position so self-evident as to rank as proof. No discussion can prove nor disprove survival of human personality after death, but it may remove some obstacles to a fair judgment and may explain the alternating "yes or no" of an individual's belief. If you have reached your decision by way of a general world-view, you may have lost interest in the outcome of such discussion. Your answer depends in general upon the type of philosophy which seems to you true. If you accept naturalism and believe that human life and consciousness are mere incidents in a world which has no unity nor purposive structure but is plain physical fact, how can you believe the survival of human personality after death of the body either possible or significant? If, however, you believe with the idealists that mind is the supreme reality, that it is not a lifeless nature which conquers the life of the body but the working of a world order which is a significant order with mind at its center—of a cosmos which is purposive—then the death of the body need not signify the annihilation of man's personality. Cessation of communication may not be final.

The conservation of valuers is threatened by death. As for the will to live—it may be a vestige of unintelligent animal tenacity for life with no definite object beyond, an instinctive clinging to certainty rather than meeting uncertainty—the desire to continue the known as long as possible rather than launch out into an unknown. It may well be taken as a sign of a deeper rationality that we wish to conserve the meanings of things as they are in this present, which can only be done by conserving the consciousness of such knowers of values as now exist.

Man is the only animal that thinks about death or expresses any doubt of its finality. This does not mean that he doubts death as a future fact. He accepts his own death and that of others as the common and inevitable lot. He plans for it and provides for the time when he will be no more among the living. But he feels the incredibility of death and questions the scope of its destruction with an incredulity which does not lessen with his years nor through the generations.

The unbelievableness of death is a common experience. This lack of belief is not due wholly to wishful thinking, though it may be partly so. One of mankind's deep intuitions is that life's realities will not be found among the obvious and superficial things, that the obvious and superficial things will not be true in their own right. He is suspicious of all obvious judgments about human destiny and questions the truth of a philosophy that presents the plain and primary facts received through sensation and perception as also the final facts. Who knows if our senses report accurately all the characteristics of the external world?

The frequent uncertainty in one's attitude toward death—the flickering yes and no, so characteristic of our times with its seeming-scientific demand for proof and verification, in contrast to the deeply buried intuitions with their equal demands—has its basis in the fact that the natural conception of death appears double and antithetical. At one moment we say death is not an end; it is an appearance only; this creative spirit cannot die. At the next, we cry, death is real; it is final; it is preposterous to think otherwise.

As witnesses of death, most of us feel this double reaction, first of all a sense of defeat and consequent desolation—defeat by all the physical forces out of which life seems to come. But also there comes to many a rebirth of confidence, a vague, hesitant, but suddenly unshakable belief—as if it had been present always in the mind, but veiled or obscured until now—a belief that there is in the universe something more than nature, which "transcends this nature of ours and holds its own in independence of what happens within nature"—something beyond destruction by death. If this resurgence of confidence is pronounced perverse by science—an emotional revulsion of feeling—there is still the conviction that we are not being led by emotion but that the emotion is the result of sudden illumination on objective fact in the structure of things. Remembering that crises of feeling are moments of intense mental activity—an instant summoning of all resources bearing upon the present experience—may it not be that more acute insight reminds man that nature is not all of the cosmic process and that it is this fact which justifies him in admitting his wishes in this matter as a modicum of evidence?

His thought takes the form of a protest that this someone else whose death has come shall not have perished. Attachments are broken off; affection is desolated. The emotional current of life is thwarted, but the protest is not against this personal pain. If youth has been taken, he should be given his chance to prove what was in him; if one of mature years, the protest is leveled against the extinction of such excellence and wisdom. Can the world which has produced such worth now dash it to oblivion? It is a cry against wastefulness in the universe; thus the idea of survival arises far more as a *claim of rightness* than as a personal wish. It is conceived as an obligation of the cosmos to itself—a right we claim to affection and to justice in the world—to purpose in the universe.

No doctrine in regard to survival does away in any case with the universal fact of death nor the suffering involved. If we are ever to be able to see beyond death, we must try first to see it as it is; we must look for what meaning it has for the race and then for the individual.

For the race, death is the evil bound up with the good which flexibility in the changes of history demands. Age grows apprehensive, lacking the courage and venturesomeness of youth. Could anything but death remove the weight of mature opinion upon the inexperience of the young? Age is both wise and prudent but tends to become rigid and static. New times demand new ways. It is death which insures that affairs shall be managed by younger minds, with hope at the controls rather than wisdom, with courage in place of tradition, with inevitable ills but also with the possibility of larger goods than have yet been brought to pass.

Lacking death, can you picture the numerical inequalities of age and youth and the constant need for emotional adjustment demanded between ancients and moderns? Parents who complain of the breach existing between generations which span less than one lifetime can hardly conceive the difficulties which might arise with a stretch of generation after generation, ad infinitum.

All the mounting importances of personal power and achievement perhaps need the natural terminus which the democracy of death best gives. Death brings the "breaks" on which the youth of today so confidently count. Death is needed to give place for birth. But can any new consciousness replace the old? The cumulative quality of individual experience increases the meaning of things. An achievement is better measured by a consciousness which knows the history of its beginnings as well as the end. Death is always teaching us that no individual is indispensable to the race nor to any of its institutions. Our need is to produce great societies from which great men come forth each in his own time.

Giving a time limit to life is like giving a frame to a painting, or a setting to any work of art. It confines it as a whole, sets it apart, so its balance and rhythms are apparent and measurable, helping us to estimate its beauty and significance. How impossible the writing of biography would be if it had to present a life-span of thousands of years! Summing up the service of an individual to his own time would indeed be an impossible task were there no end. An individual becomes completely individualized only at death. Length of days is at an end; definition is finished. The individual is a complete qualitative fact with its boundaries distinct.

So death seems to have a positive value to the race and its world. Human beings as a passing procession have advantages over human beings as a permanent assemblage, and we must acknowledge death as a benefit or even a blessing to the world.

Death is rarely a mass experience. It comes to each individual. Like a stone thrown into a quiet pond, the circles of disturbance it causes are far-reaching. To the individual who dies or who is to die, what does death mean? If one does not hold life as good, its end cannot be considered an evil. If, however, life is a good, as is held by most persons, and if in death the self is reduced to nothing, to remain forever nothing, then we bow before death as a final calamity. But a belief in ultimate annihilation casts its cloud shadow in every direction, invalidating the worth of all that has gone before and all that is to come.

Whatever his conception of death and with however much patience and fortitude a person faces it, it will be for him a lonely experience. Neither the beginning nor the end of consciousness can be realized in fact or in imagination. Probably the individual is as supremely unconscious of death as he is of birth. With age, we come to be able to convince ourselves that the common end of man will come to us as to others. We try to "put our house in order." Time, our time to do anything is now limited. Its preciousness is revealed for the first time! It is "opportunity" as never before. If only we could have realized earlier the limit of all that we as selves can do! But does our deep-seated immaturity ever become transformed into the maturity of self-knowledge without the ripening years to help it to fruition? The realized limit of life helps to reconstruct purposes and to prepare for destiny while producing a lively interest in prolonging life and perhaps in transposing its unfinished tasks beyond death. These later years often bring an increased sensitiveness to spiritual values as well as added infirmities and weariness of the body.

Life produces both bodily and mental conditions for its own closing. We are told of the biological life cycle as a ripening of all the complex processes of the body, but we recognize too a mental life cycle which has little to do with the frailties of the aging body. Life becomes cluttered with detail, irrelevancies, irrationalities. The natural reaction for freeing one's self from this seemingly needless but inevitable load and burden is to become aloof, to let life go by, without responding with the customary affiliations with, loyalties to, and immersions in, the events of the day and of the times. Life at its zenith gives itself to its current stream of history, its own time and problems, its own passion for rightness. It becomes identified with this special issue, this struggling group, this spirited cause.

In age, we recognize all these loyalties but fail to be moved to take part in them. The will with its efficiency remains untouched by the need of combat; spectatorship is a new accomplishment based on a longing that it may lead to serenity. The possibility of death takes on the new significance of freedom from all this load of needs in which one takes no part, this burden of meaninglessness which accompanies the growth of all meaning. It is a natural preparation for the renunciation of life to the realities of death. The universality of death is part of the essential brotherhood of man, a leveler of his conflicts. John Donne tells us in "Devotions upon Emergent Occasions,"

> No man is an *Iland,* intire of it selfe; every man is a peece of the *Continent,* a part of the *maine;* if a *Clod* bee washed away by the *Sea,* Europe is the lesse, as well as if a *Promontorie* were, as well as if a *Mannor* of thy *friends* or of *thine own* were; any mans death diminishes me, because I am involved in *Mankinde;* And therefore never send to know for whom the bell tolls; it tolls for *thee.*

There are changing concepts of death. The faith in survival of death was formerly diversified by doubt. Now it often seems to be doubt which is diversified by faith. In all times, there are current beliefs in such matters which most individuals accept without thinking them through. We need to recognize that there are these fashions in belief as well as in attire and other customs. Their basis may be less arbitrary, but it is human to adopt without much modification a current style whatever its inconsistencies, even to the extent of personal discomfort.

In the present time, the current belief is influenced by a seeming-scientific tradition that nothing should be believed that cannot be proved through the senses—verified by competent witnesses. Yet faith underlies one of the basic assumptions of science that man's senses report fully and accurately all characteristics of the external world.

We now know that senses have to be extended to reach great masses of accepted facts. This acceptance again requires faith. Like the faith placed in a compass when on the high seas or the faith underlying a credit system, it has been repeatedly justified by results. Our respect for science and its momentous service to mankind makes us forget that the special sciences have nothing to say about life as a whole nor the world as a whole. They cannot tell us what life is, nor electricity, nor gravity, nor relativity. Their business is to find out how these realities behave. They make no collective statement that all of reality is included in what they survey. Scientific work carries with it a strong conviction that natural law rules all happenings without exception. Survival of death may be natural law, but we have lost communication with all the witnesses; so science, as such, has nothing to say about it.

No scientist understands why light affects silver bromide, but the fact that it does is the pivot of ignorance on which one of our great and rapidly developing industries turns. It is as if science were busy taking the world apart like a great mechanism; we need to know the behavior of every detail of its parts, in order to control its motions, to turn it to our uses, to repair its inevitable wear. It is not the business of science to put it all together again—nor to ponder, as science, upon its purpose, its period of usefulness, its designer, nor its destiny. These aspects of the world lie in the fields of philosophy and religion each of which regards its certainties as secure as are those of science.

Many religions have been concerned with the matter of survival of death. In the great ceremony of putting away the dead in all early religions (if not in all religions) there is institutional denial that nature has conquered. Almost without exception in primitive ceremonies, there is some provision made, often at great material sacrifice, for the journeying soul; so it has been a costly belief.

Can we explain this conviction of survival? Is it a human tendency to see as true what we would like to believe? Or is it an intuition, sharpened by the poignancy of grief and despair which results in a change of perspective on the objective vista of things—a way of looking at things which supplements the facts of experience, rounding out and conserving our deepest values? It is as if the decision belonged in a region in which the felt values of things legislate for our sense of truth, as they may in religion.

Unlike the early Egyptians, the early Hebrews record no belief of the survival of death. Sheol, where shades survived, was "a land of silence and forgetfulness." The idea of Gehenna, where the wicked were tormented, came later in Hebrew thought. The conception of continued life for the "good" followed as a condition for immortality which has persisted throughout Christianity. The phrase "immortality of the soul" is not found in the Bible. The historic account of the resurrection of Jesus is the foundation of Christian faith in the survival of death. There is no evidence that Jesus thought the soul inherently immortal. His teaching of "Whoever liveth and believeth in me shall never die" is a conditioned continuance of life which the apostles also taught.

The permanence of the human spirit and its continuing growth and evolution is not to be determined by science nor by theology. It is bound up with the significance of life and life's individualization of consciousness—with the meaning of the universe and the indestructibility of its consciousness—with the world-view of mind and its relation to the creative process.

If your philosophy admits a belief that there is something in the cosmic order which is essentially eternal, you must also be able to believe that there may be conditions under which the human self *shares in this quality.* If individual consciousness does not survive, is there any indestructibility? Are the senseless things the only lasting realities while a human being, who alone can know his own existence, is but a passing show? Can the less real endure while the most real is destroyed?

If death is not an end, is it a transition from dependence on one set of conditions to adjustments within another? Will it mean another period of development through apprenticeship with its fumbling aims and labored strokes, or will it mean the practice of a maturer art with surer vision and freer brush? No one can tell. Unless it means growth with fresh vigor, and revised directive, perfected understanding, would it be a satisfying life?

In his chapter, "What Ought to Be" in *Thoughts on Death and Life,* Hocking points out that

> . . . survival of death is a possibility but not a necessity of destiny. . . . The quality of the human self, as I conceive it, is not immortality but immortability, the conditional possibility of survival. . . .
>
> Neither does any man know fully through self-consciousness what in himself might render him viable beyond death. He does not so much as know what it is that keeps him alive in his present situation. It must be something simple, for it is so natural to live, to think, to be—so little of an effort—so little a possible object of effort. He knows something, at any rate, of what it is not: it is not natural prowess, nor acquired capacities, nor any proud work of the excursive self. If anything can see him through the crisis of death, it will be as near to him as breathing and as elusive as that which now keeps him in being. If there are conditions for survival, they must be as simple as the saying "As a man thinketh (of himself) in his heart, so is he," and as natural as the passage by growth from one stage of readiness to another. . . .
>
> Survival may be a matter of the degree of reality which the self attains. For the reality of the self is not a fixed quantity; the self is more or less real, more or less a cherisher of illusion, more or less sham and pretense and self-deceit; the deepest law of duty is to put off falsities and achieve what reality we are capable of. . . .
>
> For death is not the erasure of life by an entity called "Death," nor by an entity called "Nature." Death is an encounter of the real with the Real; and the Real, whatever it is, is conscious and living, not inanimate.

Perhaps this is all we need to know of the ways and conditions of survival; but what we chiefly know is that it *ought to be*. For unless there is a way for the continuance of the human self, the world is full of the blunt edges of human meanings, the wreckage of human values, and therefore of the failures of God.[54]

Notes

1. Harlow Shapley, *Galaxies* (Cambridge: Harvard University Press, 1943).
2. Henry Harris Russell, 1940. Permission given by editors of *Scientific American.*
3. Permission given in a letter from Dr. H. Bethe, University of California, Los Alamos Scientific Laboratory.
4. Reprinted from Taylor, Lawrence, and Langmuir, *Molecular Films the Cyclotron and the New Biology,* p. 64, with the permission of the Rutgers University Press. Copyrighted 1942, 1946 by the Trustees of Rutgers College in New Jersey.
5. Fred Hoyle, *Nature of the Universe* (New York: Harper & Brothers, 1951).
6. Sir Charles Sherrington, *Man on His Nature,* Gifford Lectures (New York: Cambridge University Press, 1941 and 1951), p. 251.
7. John Masefield, "Life" with permission from *Atlantic Monthly.*
8. Reported by Waldemar Kaempffert in *Explorations in Science* (New York: Viking Press, 1953).
9. Walter de la Mare, "Miss T," *Collected Poems* (New York: Henry Holt & Co., 1920). Copyright 1948 by Walter de la Mare. Used by permission of the publishers.
10. Erwin Schrödinger, *What Is Life?* (New York: Cambridge University Press, 1947), p. 80, 81, 86.
11. James Young Simpson, *Landmarks in the Struggle between Science and Religion* (New York: Harper & Brothers), p. 174, 176.
12. Sir Arthur Keith, A New Introduction to *Origin of Species,* Everyman's Library Edition (New York: E. P. Dutton & Co., 1928).

13. This book was *Vestiges of the Natural History of Creation* by Robert Chambers (1802-1871), author and joint original partner of the Edinburgh publishing firm of W. R. Chambers.
14. Reginald Ruggles Gates, *Human Ancestry,* Preface (Cambridge: Harvard University Press, 1948).
15. William McNeile Dixon, *The Human Situation,* Gifford Lectures (New York: Longmans, Green & Co., Inc., 1935-1937).
16. Warren and Carmichael, *Elements of Human Psychology* (Boston: Houghton Mifflin Co.), p. 442.
17. Julian Huxley, *Fortune,* 1942.
18. Sir Charles Sherrington, *Man on His Nature,* Gifford Lectures, 1941.
19. Sir Charles Sherrington, *Rede Lecture* (New York: Cambridge University Press, 1937), p. 7.
20. Sir Arthur Eddington, *The Nature of the Physical World* (New York: Cambridge University Press), p. 293.
21. Sherrington, *Man on His Nature,* p. 268.
22. Charles S. Myers, *Hobhouse Lectures* (New York: Oxford University Press, 1937); *Realm of Mind* (Oxford University Press).
23. Sherrington, *Man on His Nature,* p. 357.
24. William Ernest Hocking, *Types of Philosophy* (New York: Charles Scribner's Sons, 1939), p. 98-100.
25. Ernst Haeckel, "Psychic Gradations," *The Riddle of the Universe* (1899).
26. Charles Sedgewick Minot, President of the American Association for the Advancement of Science, 1902 Presidential Address.
27. Herbert S. Jennings, *Behavior of the Lower Organisms* (New York: The Macmillan Co.).
28. Sir Charles Sherrington, Nobel Prize work on *The Integrative Action of the Nervous System* (New Haven: Yale University Press, 1906), p. 390.
29. Wolfgang Kohler, *Mentality of Apes* (New York: Harcourt, Brace & Co.), p. 298.
30. *Ibid.,* p. 318.
31. Robert Yerkes, *Chimpanzees* (New Haven: Yale University Press, 1943), p. 171.
32. Nils Bohr, "Light and Life," a lecture on Light Therapy at the International Congress in Copenhagen, August 15, 1932, published in *Nature* by Cambridge University Press.
33. Hocking, *Types of Philosophy,* p. 7.
34. Eddington, *The Nature of the Physical World,* p. 335.
35. Hocking, *Types of Philosophy,* p. 114.

36. William Ernest Hocking, *Science and the Idea of God* (Chapel Hill: University of North Carolina Press, 1943), p. 106.
37. *Ibid.*, p. 108.
38. *New York Times Magazine,* December 4, 1949.
39. Josiah Royce, *Lectures on Modern Idealism* (New Haven: Yale University Press, 1923), p. 2.
40. Hocking, *Types of Philosophy,* p. 333.
41. C. G. Jung, *Modern Man in Search of a Soul* (New York: Harcourt, Brace & Co.), p. 264.
42. E. B. Wilson, *The Cell* (New York: The Macmillan Co., 1924), p. 1117.
43. W. McNeile Dixon, *The Human Situation* (London: St. Martin's Press, Inc.), pp. 144-145.
44. Irwin Edman, *Four Ways of Philosophy* (New York: Henry Holt & Co.), p. 85.
45. Crane Brinton, *Ideas and Men* (New York: Prentice-Hall, Inc., 1950), p. 533.
46. Hugh Stott Taylor, *Molecular Films the Cyclotron and the New Biology,* p. 24 and 26.
47. Dixon, *The Human Situation,* p. 34, 36.
48. Robert A. Millikan, *Autobiography* (New York: Prentice-Hall), p. 289.
49. Albert Einstein, *The World as I See It* (New York: Philosophical Library, Inc.).
50. Eddington, *The Nature of the Physical World,* p. 322.
51. Robert A. Millikan, *Science and Life* (Boston: Pilgrim Press), p. 59.
52. W. M. Dixon, *The Human Situation,* The Gifford Lectures, 1935-1937 (New York: Cambridge University Press), p. 436.
53. Hocking, Memorial Service for Dr. Neal at Tufts College.
54. Hocking, *Thoughts on Death and Life* (New York: Harper & Brothers, 1937) from chapter, "What Ought to Be."

Index